Oriental Paths to Health

C000193103

By the same author

Reclaiming the Wisdom of the Body
A Guide to Acupuncture (with Peter Firebrace)

Oriental Paths to Health

A guide to ancient wisdom and practice

Sandra Hill

CONSTABLE • LONDON

First published in Great Britain 2000
by Constable, an imprint of Constable & Robinson Ltd
3 The Lanchesters, 162 Fulham Palace Road
London W6 9ER

A CIP Catalogue record for this book is available from the British
Library.

Acknowledgements

I would like to thank all my teachers, especially Dr Hiroshi Motoyama, Claude Larre SJ and Elisabeth Rochat de la Vallée; Penny Neal-Smith, Sylvia Prescott, Xi Xing Wang, Kiyomi Kuratani. I am indebted to everyone who comes to see me in the clinic — as this is where the real learning takes place. A special thank you to Ian and Joe, Mary and John for all your love and support.

SH

Contents

Introduction

Throughout this book we will explore the Chinese concepts of health and transformation; of individual destiny and how it relates to our health and general well-being. We will learn simple traditional exercises, meditations and breathing techniques to help us transform and move on; to keep our feet firmly on the ground, and our spirits open to heaven.

In classical times, when the first writings on Chinese medicine were collated, there was no distinction made between physical, emotional and spiritual health. Emotional and spiritual causes were often seen to lie behind physical disease. The early medical texts were influenced by the Daoist classics, which stressed the discovery of one's true nature, by alignment with the Dao – the way of heaven. The Daoist classics insist that the process of constant change and transformation is crucial for life and growth. Later the Daoist alchemical teachings, possibly influenced by Indian thought as tantric Buddhist texts were introduced into China, took this further and suggested practices to transform the energies within the body in order to enhance the natural process of personal evolution.

Many of the ideas represented in the first part of the book are based on the *Yellow Emperor's Inner Classic* (or *Classic of Internal Medicine, Huangdi Nei Jing*) which collated many earlier writings and oral teachings at the beginning of the Han Dynasty in approximately 220 BC. This is the main source of information about Chinese medicine and is still learnt by heart by many scholars of medicine in China today. The

Han Dynasty was the fruition of early Chinese culture. Territories torn apart during the Warring States period were united under one ruler. The Chinese calligraphic script was formalised and knowledge was communicated for the first time throughout a united Chinese Empire. With a common written language and a territory united, the Han Dynasty laid the foundations of Chinese civilisation which was to continue for the next two millennia. Many teachings were committed to writing which had previously been passed by word of mouth. The great Chinese classical texts of the *Yi Jing* (*Book of Change*), the *Shi Jing* (*Book of History*), *Li Jing* (*Book of Rites*) and the *Nei Jing* (*Inner Classic*) were collated and collected in the libraries of the rich and powerful, as were the teachings of Confucius, Lao zi and Zhuang zi. Buddhist teachings were also beginning to infiltrate south-west China from India, bringing a rich diversity of ideas and practices. This was an exciting time in the formation of consciousness. Old shamanic traditions and Confucian order lived side by side, and the medicine of the *Yellow Emperor's Classic* reflects the many diverse ideas and interests of the time, and in particular the predominant philosophical world view of the Daoists.

The philosophy which dominated Han Dynasty China was common to government, medicine and spiritual practice. No distinction was made between the rules that govern the physical, intellectual or spiritual realities of life. During the early Han Dynasty mankind was seen as living between the powers of heaven and earth: earth bringing physicality and nourishment, heaven bringing the cycles of time and contact with the spirits. Life was possible only through the constant intermingling of the energies of heaven and earth, yin and yang, fire and water. The *Yellow Emperor's Inner Classic* reflects this world view, taking the form of a dialogue between the Yellow Emperor, Huang di, and his minister, Qi bo. The Emperor asks the questions, and Qi bo provides the answers. It is presented in two parts, the Su wen, or Simple Questions, and the Ling shu, or Spiritual Pivot. At the beginning of the first chapter of the Su wen, the Emperor asks his minister: 'How is it that men and women no longer live to be a hundred years old like the men and women of antiquity?' And the minister replies:

The men and women of antiquity followed the Way.
They modelled themselves on yin and yang
And attained harmony of mind and body.

Each of these early chapters is ordered according to its numerological significance: chapter 2, for example, describes duality and the movement of yin and yang, chapter 4 is a presentation of the four seasons and their effect on health, chapter 5 an introduction to the five elements. The classical Chinese texts often use numerology to describe the unfolding of life: one representing the Dao, the undivided oneness that precedes all life; nine, the number of completion. All the Chinese classical texts have eighty-one chapters, which, as the square of nine, symbolises ultimate completion. By looking at classical Chinese numerology we can begin to grasp some of the basic philosophical ideas behind the medicine. Within the Chinese philosophy of life reality is presented in many different ways. The old texts tend to play with ideas and concepts rather than make rules and regulations, and the language is more that of poetry than of science. The following associations are based on a symbology of numbers. I hope that they will provide a simple introduction to unfamiliar terms and concepts. A glossary is provided at the back of the book for further reference.

One –	the Dao, the one, the unmanifest, the true nature.
Two –	yin and yang, matter and energy, the principles of earth and heaven:
Yin –	that which reflects the qualities of the earth, cooling, moistening, nourishing.
Yang –	that which reflects the qualities of heaven: warming, moving, transforming.
Three –	the three energy centres and the three treasures:
Jing –	material essence, informational coding, sperm and ovum.
Qi –	that which moves between heaven and earth: energy, movement, transformation.
Shen –	immaterial spirit, consciousness, grace.
Four –	the four directions and the four seasons:
East –	spring, beginnings, movement, change.
South –	summer, fruition, aspiration, openness.
West –	autumn, closing in, weighing up, letting go.
North –	winter, completion, hibernation, preparation.
Five –	the five elements, climates, movements and the five internal organs:
Fire –	heat, upward movement; the heart and circulatory system.
Water –	cold, downward movement; the kidneys and reproductive system.
Earth –	damp, rotational movement; the spleen and stomach, the digestive system.
Wood –	wind, outward movement; the liver and system of movement and freeflow.

Metal –	dry, inward movement; the lungs and respiratory system.
Six –	the six divisions of yin and yang: the meridian system:
Tai Yin –	greater yin, the meridians of the spleen and lungs.
Jue Yin –	absolute yin, the meridians of the liver and heart master.
Shao Yin –	lesser yin, the meridians of the heart and kidneys.
Tai Yang –	greater yang, the meridians of the bladder and small intestine.
Yang Ming –	brilliant yang, the meridians of the stomach and large intestine.
Shao Yang –	lesser yang, the meridians of the gall bladder and triple burner, or metabolic function.
Seven –	the seven inner movements of qi, the seven emotions:
Joy and elation –	qi rises upwards.
Fear –	qi moves downwards.
Anger --	qi moves upwards and outwards.
Grief and sadness –	qi moves inwards.
Worry and obsession –	qi knots.
Oppression –	qi presses down on the heart.
Fright –	qi is scattered.
Eight –	the eight divisions of space: the eight winds, the eight trigrams, the eight extraordinary meridians.

Nine –	The three treasures multiplied by the three energy centres: the completion of movement and transformation.

If we take a closer look at the sequence of numbers we can see that with each odd number there is an expansion of energy, a movement towards change, with each even number a consolidation of form. This process of expansion and consolidation is central to all Chinese thought and can be easily illustrated by our life experience. As we grow and change we need time to adapt to the new situation. If our growth is sudden, we often become out of balance, and this may be reflected in illness. Similarly, if we remain too long in one place, inhibiting our natural inclination for transformation, our energy will become static and blocked, again creating imbalance and possibly illness. It is important to create a balance between times of movement, change and growth and times of assimilation, consolidation and reflection.

The Chinese often illustrate this natural movement of life by the bamboo, which grows upward, and then stops for a time of consolidation, gathering its strength and resources for its next stage of growth. These knots of energy are seen to be the basis of its extraordinary strength. The bamboo is so commonly seen in Chinese art and decoration as it serves as a reminder of these basic truths. At each phase of growth it is necessary to make contact with our roots, to remain in touch with our source, and come closer to our true nature.

The first part of this book will present an explanation of the energetic foundations of health, drawing on the teachings of the classical Chinese medical texts. It will also explore the energy body, as seen by the Daoist alchemists. The second part will make comparisons with the traditional Indian system. The third will suggest practical methods to aid the process of change and transformation.

My interest in Chinese medicine began over thirty years ago, when a yoga teacher proposed a connection between the yoga asanas and the meridians of Chinese acupuncture. A few years later I travelled to India and then to Japan, where I studied martial arts and shiatsu, before embarking on two years of intensive training with Dr Hiroshi Motoyama, whose in-depth knowledge of the subtle energy systems of both the Chinese and Indian traditions became the focus of both my study and my practice. My training in Japan was experiential. I did not attend lectures, take notes, study into the early hours – but I did practise yoga and meditation and I learned to experience within my body, to put ideas to the test, to weigh up the validity of what I learned by testing it out on myself.

Since my return to the UK over twenty years ago I have studied and practised Chinese medicine. As always, I am indebted to Claude Larre SJ and Elisabeth Rochat de la Vallée of The Ricci Institute, Paris, for their deep and inspiring teaching of the Chinese medical classics. My work continues to be enriched by cross-references with the Indian system of chakras and nadis and the philosophical depths of Hinduism. For this I draw on the tantric teachings of Swami Satyananda Saraswati of the Bihar School of Yoga, and on the inspiration of Sri Aurobindo and 'The Mother', who became the spiritual focus of the Aurobindo ashram in Pondicherry following the former's death in 1950. But it is Dr Hiroshi Motoyama whom I must thank for first intro-ducing me to these ideas and for initiating my practice, as it is by putting ideas into practice that transformation is achieved. In spanning the realms of science and spirituality as both Shinto priest and research scientist, Dr Motoyama has facilitated the joining of two realities so often kept separate in our modern world. His teachings draw together those of tantric Hinduism and Daoist alchemy, investigative research with direct experience of spiritual reality. The years I spent in Tokyo provided a firm basis for my future study of Chinese medicine, and opened the door to a world of much greater dimensions than I ever imagined possible.

As science fast approaches the subtle realms, and spirituality shakes itself free of the constraints of religion, we may begin to understand more of the unseen and unknowable. In the meantime let us attempt to share our information, to make it more available and accessible. As practitioners it is our duty to share our information with our patients. As patients it is our right to demand information from our doctors and therapists. We are no longer in the age of secret knowledge and hierarchies of power. Knowledge is to be shared. It is my hope that this book goes some way towards that end.

Part One
Living Between Heaven and Earth

Human beings model themselves on earth,
Earth models itself on heaven,
Heaven models itself on the Dao,
And the Dao on that which is natural.
Lao zi, *Dao de jing*, Ch. 25

Within the classical Chinese medical tradition good health assumes a health of body, mind and spirit. It also assumes a continual act of becoming, rather than a static state of being. According to Lao zi, following the Dao requires the ability to move forward with each changing circumstance, to be free of preconceptions and habits which may keep us bound up in old patterns of behaviour, old ways of looking at reality. Following the Dao is nothing other than following the true nature of things, or living according to our true nature. Daoism maintains that if we follow the Dao, if we follow our true nature, life will flow through us without resistance.

It is resistance to life, the resistance to change and transformation, which tends to create disease. The ancient Chinese stressed that good health is a process of change and adaptation, not a state of perfection to be reached, but the ability to change and flow with the circumstances of life as we grow towards our future. This is not merely poetic symbolism, but a practical description of the way life works. Modern biochemistry tells us that physical life is a process of continual movement and transformation. The food that we eat and the air that we breathe are transformed within the body to produce energy in the process of cellular metabolism. Food is either assimilated by the tissues and rebuilt into complex materials or broken down for energy release in the process of cellular respiration. Each cell in the body is continually engaged in this process, even the cells of the most inert structures such as the bones are in a continual state of activity. It is cellular metabolism that is the identifying characteristic of all living systems and it is the ability of certain living systems to perform this operation with increasing efficiency which provides them with sufficient energy to grow and change, adapt and evolve.

Basic biology also tells us that within any living organism, one kind of energy can be converted to another kind of energy in a process which is called thermodynamics. The simplest example of this kind of energy transformation is the ability of green plants to take energy from the sun in the form of light and convert it into chemical energy through the process of photosynthesis. When the Chinese speak of energy and energy transformation, it is this kind of thing that they have in mind. Within animals the processes are more complex, but this basic model of the plant drawing its nutrients from the earth and its source of energy from the sun is the simplest way to understand the model developed by the ancient Chinese to explain the transformation of energy within the human being (Plate 1).

In Han Dynasty China mankind was described as living between the energies of heaven and earth: earth providing nutrition in the form of food and water, heaven providing warmth and light from the sun. Their approach to medicine was an attempt to understand the way in which energy was created and transformed within the body. And although the basis was extremely simple, they identified a complex process of change and transformation, based on the dynamic

Plate 1

interaction of nutrition and respiration. They also identified certain inherent substances which enabled these processes to take place, and which may be likened to the catalysts identified by biologists as essential for these processes to proceed efficiently. This so-called 'production of energy' is at the basis of Chinese medicine, and the enhancement of this process is at the basis of Chinese yoga.

Before we look more closely at the production of energy, let us take some time to examine how the energies of heaven and earth are evident, both in nature and in the individual, as the interdependent couples of yin and yang, water and fire, essence and spirit.

YIN AND YANG

yang transforms the qi
yin perfects the form
Yellow Emperor's Inner Classic, Simple Questions, Ch. 5

By careful observation of nature, the ancient Chinese observed that life is possible through the mingling of heaven and earth, of light and heat from the sun and nutrition from the earth, and that these two forces maintain a dynamic balance, which creates constant movement and change. They called the action of these dynamic opposites yin and yang: yin representing the earth, and the qualities of stability and form; yang representing heaven and the qualities of light and heat. The dynamic interaction of heaven and earth creates energy or qi.

Yin and yang are often represented by two dragons, one red symbolising heaven and yang, and one black symbolising the earth and yin. Intertwined they represent life, apart they symbolise death. Life on earth is only possible through the intermingling of yin and yang, the forces of heaven and earth. Earth may be yin and heaven may be yang, but all the phenomena between heaven and earth are composed of a continually changing pattern of yin and yang tendencies, no one thing being totally yin or yang, but rather having an energetic tendency towards one or the other. Within a system, if yang increases there comes a point of instability where there is a natural decline and a return of yin.

In order to illustrate this continual movement between yin and yang the Chinese classics often refer to the cycle of the seasons throughout the year. Midsummer, when the days are long and there is maximum exposure to the light and to the sun, is the time of greatest yang. Heat is at its height, and energy moves towards the exterior, which in the plant world is expressed in flowering and blossoming. Midwinter, the time of the shortest day and minimum sunlight, is the time of greatest yin; the earth is cold and the energy retreats to the interior. In the plant world the seed is buried deep within the earth, the sap withdrawn to the interior of the plant. Yet within that time of absolute yin there is all the potential for new life and growth which will appear in spring, and within the flowering and creation of fruit there is the inevitable decline and decay of the autumn. The tai ji symbol illustrates this movement of growth and decline well. The white dot of yang within the black mass of absolute yin, and the black dot of yin within the white mass of pure yang suggest that within each there is the seed of the opposite (Plate 2).

The spring is known as young yang, the summer as old yang; the autumn as young yin, the winter as old yin. This pattern of waxing and waning may be applied to all natural cycles: the cycle of the day, from dawn, through midday, when the sun is at its height, to sunset and midnight and also the cycle of life, from birth through youth and middle age, to old age and finally death, and of course the phases of the moon.

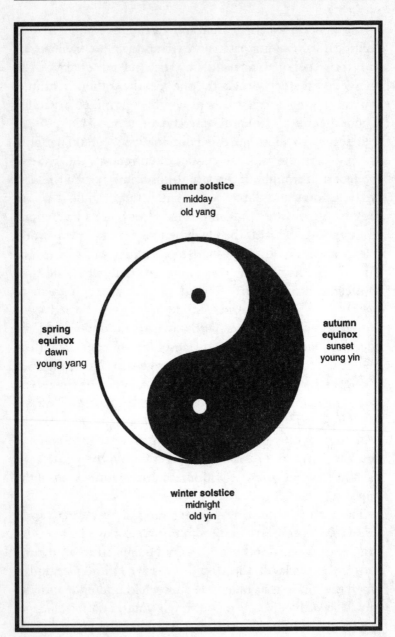

summer solstice
midday
old yang

spring
equinox
dawn
young yang

autumn
equinox
sunset
young yin

winter solstice
midnight
old yin

Plate 2

The observation of yin and yang throughout the cycles of nature also shows a movement towards the exterior with the yang part of the cycle and towards the interior with the yin. Within the body, this is also one of the important attributes of yin and yang. Yang governs the exterior, or the movement towards the exterior, yin governs the interior or the movement towards the interior. The cooling, calming and nutritive effects of yin are said to be drawn from the earth towards the interior of the body by way of the yin channels; the warming, energising effects of yang are said to be drawn from above via the yang channels. It is the balancing of energy within these yin and yang channels which lies at the basis of acupuncture and Chinese massage and exercise. There are six yin channels which have a cooling, moistening and nourishing action, reflecting the qualities of the earth, six yang channels which have a warming, energising and transforming action, reflecting the qualities of heaven. The yin meridians have their meeting points and main areas of influence deep within the abdomen and deep within the chest, from where they nurture the internal organs and the body fluids. The yang meridians have their meeting points on the face, particularly around the upper orifices, the eyes, the ears, the nose and the mouth. The yang action is always towards the exterior, and the yang meridians contact the orifices and enable the exchange with the exterior through the senses. They allow us to see, hear, taste, smell and also to speak (Plate 3).

Behind these main yin and yang channels lies another, deeper regulatory system of pathways, which are said to govern development and growth. Within the mother's womb the new life is moulded according to the laws of yin and yang, through the action of what are known as the 'eight extraordinary meridians'. These channels create the perfect energetic shape which acts as a guide for the full development of the physical body. They are particularly active during the

17

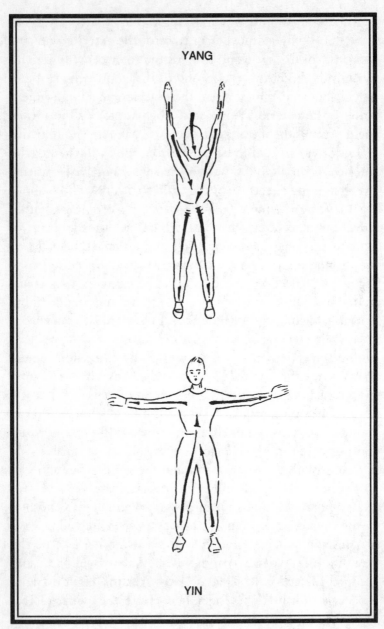

Plate 3

18

formation of the organism within the womb, but remain as a kind of energetic blueprint throughout life. They are responsible for the perfection of the form and the inner regulation of yin and yang.

These primary energy channels remain the principal guidelines for both the original formation of the body, and its renewal throughout our lives; the yang representing the energetic life force, the yin the ability to create and renew physical form. Yin and yang are totally interdependent, and not one single bodily function can occur without their interaction. Without yin, yang has no physical basis; without yang, yin has no means of expression. We nourish yin by the food that we eat and our contact with the earth; we nurture yang with our breath and our contact with heaven. From food and the process of food metabolism we make the material essences to build and sustain our physical form; from the air we breathe we take in oxygen to facilitate this process of breakdown and assimilation and the release of energy via the process of cellular respiration.

We all tend to have our own individual metabolic pattern which may reflect a tendency towards yin or yang. This may be our constitutional inheritance, or due to our lifestyle, in particular our eating, sleeping and exercising habits. The close observation of life in action formed the basis of the Chinese understanding of health and also provided a system and a language to identify where things go wrong. The preponderance of one quality over another was observed to create imbalance – too much yin and there may be sluggishness, coldness, dampness and inertia. Too much yang and there may be restlessness, heat, dryness and even mania. If the body fails to make the necessary adjustments, intervention may be necessary. Within traditional Chinese medicine looking at lifestyle, diet and exercise would always accompany treatment with either acupuncture or herbs. Unless the cause of the imbalance is traced any gain from treatment may only be temporary.

Understanding our metabolic type is an important first step in any process of self-transformation. If we have a tendency to be slow, sluggish and to gain weight, we need more yang – more activity. If we have a tendency to be speedy, never able to relax, we need more yin, more rest and to give more attention to our nutrition. Although this is a simplification of the intricate interactions of yin and yang within the body and psyche, it is at this level that we begin with Chinese medical diagnosis. Before we are able to address our current imbalance and undertake a process of self-transformation we must accept who we are and the reality of our present situation. We can only begin with ourselves.

FIRE AND WATER

The qualities of yin and yang are often compared with the actions and interactions of fire and water in nature, and Chinese art and poetry use fire and water symbolically to suggest the movements and transformations of yin and yang. Water is described as submissive, retreating and weak, fire as devouring and transforming, but it is the very stillness and passivity of water that eventually overcomes all obstacles. In the words of Lao zi:

> In the world there is nothing more submissive and weak
>   than water.
> Yet for attacking that which is hard and strong nothing
>   can take its place.

Water is capable of taking the shape of any container; it is without form, but able to take form. It can be still and quiet but also reacts quickly to any movement or agitation. It responds to winds and currents, but easily returns to stillness once they have subsided. Water can also exist in three forms, as a solid, a liquid or a gas. It is therefore the most adaptable substance. It constantly moves and changes with no attachment.

The cycle of water reflects all cycles of nature. From deep within the earth water emerges at the surface and slowly makes its way to the sea. Nothing can prevent this movement. It may take time, but water has no sense of hurry. It will wait until it is able to flow around any obstacle in its way. Attracted by the warmth of the sun it vaporises to form clouds, which eventually release water in the form of rain to moisten the earth. Because it is seen to come from the earth and return to the earth in a continual cycle it is often used as a metaphor for life.

The action of water upon the surface of the earth helps to create the shape of the land, and the Chinese often used the language of the action of water to describe the flow of energy within the body. The acupuncture meridians are described as having a well, a source, a stream, and a sea point. Acupuncture points are often described as caverns, hollows, marshes and ravines, which describes the nature of the energy flow at a particular location. The source has a particular significance, as it is said to link us to the origin, the undivided oneness that lies beyond the complexity of life on earth. The water at the source or spring is new, reborn after its descent through the earth. In the earliest descriptions of the five elements, water is the origin. It is formless, and only in interaction with fire and earth can create form.

Within Chinese medicine the water element controls the lower abdomen, and the organs of the kidneys and the bladder. But as well as the more obvious control of water metabolism within the body, the function of the kidneys in Chinese medicine also includes the adrenal glands and the sexual hormones. They govern fertility, growth and development and act as our connection to the origin of life. As the kidneys are a double organ, they are often said to represent both aspects of water, quiet stillness, and powerful agitation, both the hard and the soft. The kidneys govern the bones and the ability to stand upright, but also the spinal cord, the bone marrow and synovial fluids. Their strength is seen in the teeth but also in the hair. They govern the preservation of life, but also give the ability to create a new life. Their season is the winter and they are represented by the image of the seed stored deep within the earth. The kidneys store essence, which in its most physical form refers to sexual secretions, and in its most rarefied, it is the most refined, the most subtle form of matter.

The colour associated with the water element is blue-black, the energetic movement is downwards, the associated emotion is fear. But it is through facing our fears that we gain wisdom, and wisdom is also associated with the kidneys and the water element. This knowledge or wisdom suggests a grounding in life experience and a practical ability to live one's life. It is a knowing that is in touch with the body and the senses, as much instinctual as intellectual.

Fire is the second element, and it represents trans-formation. The primary aspect of fire is the sun, its secondary aspect is the fire within the core of the earth. Fire is the destroyer, but also the force that is able to release energy from matter. It destroys form but also it can fix form. The mixture of water and earth to make clay is made permanent by exposing it to heat and fire. Fire also moulds and shapes metals, allowing one form to dissolve and another to be created. Fire is necessary for all transformation. It is the energy of the sun which attracts the water from the seas to create clouds and rain. It is the fire under the cooking pot which allows us easier access to the energy within food.

The interaction of fire and water provides a rich source of imagery for the Chinese and also gives the basis for a symbolic language to describe the transformations which occur within the body. The process of energy metabolism is symbolised by the image of the cauldron, in which water is heated by fire until it is vaporised or refined. In nature water has a downward movement, it always seeks the lowest place, whereas fire moves upwards. Water is cooling, fire heating. Their mutual interaction ensures that they maintain a balance. Too much fire and the water may boil dry, too much water and the fire will not remain alight.

We have seen that in Chinese medicine the water element is related to the lower abdomen, and is associated with the kidneys and the sexual organs. The fire element controls the chest and is associated with the heart. But there are two aspects of fire in nature, and this is also the case within the body. The heavenly fire is related to the heart, and refers to spirit; the earthly fire is the fire of transformation which is related to the abdomen. This earthly fire aids digestion and assimilation and together with the water and essence of the lower abdomen creates the energy for fertility, development and growth. It is associated with all processes of change and transformation and is closely linked to the idea of the catalyst in the energy transformation process. This mixing of fire and water in the lower abdomen enables us to create a new life and also to continually renew and rebuild our own life.

In Chinese medicine the heart has a double charge, it controls the circulation of blood and provides a residence for spirit. Any discussion of the heart within Chinese medicine will always assume this double meaning of the heart in its physical aspect and also as the residence of pure spirit. A quiet and peaceful heart is necessary for spirit to be present. The Daoist classics often talk of an empty heart as the prerequisite for attracting the spirit. This is not an emptiness which suggests coldness and indifference, but a heart that is always ready to be filled. In the same way that the physical heart must remain empty and open to allow the constant filling and refilling of the blood, so the energetic centre of the heart must be open and free from blockages and restriction to allow the free movement of emotion and spirit.

The season linked with the fire element is summer – the time of openness and expansion. The colour associated with the fire element is red, the energetic movement is upwards. Its associated emotion is joy. Too much joy, or over-excitement moves the energy upwards and the spirits may be scattered. The water element has a natural movement downwards, the fire element upwards. As heat is controlled by cooling, and cold by heating, so also the fear associated with the kidneys which makes the energy descend, can be balanced by the uplifting joy of the heart; an excessive upsurge of excitement can be grounded by the wisdom inherent within the kidneys.

Within the system of the five elements and their energetic movements within the body it is fire and water which play a major role in the process of change and transformation. Although all the elements are seen to have a mutual interaction of creation and destruction, fire and water form the vertical axis on which the others rely, and represent those aspects of regeneration, fertility and evolution of consciousness which lie at the basis of Daoist yoga and alchemy. The heart and the kidneys are responsible for the safe-keeping of the most subtle aspects of life. The kidneys store the essences (jing) and the heart stores the spirits (shen). Together the essences and spirits express the life force. The essences are yin and belong to the earth and to the physical structure, the spirits are yang and belong to heaven and to consciousness. Their interactions are mediated by the qi, the vital energy within the breath. Jing, qi and shen, essences, breaths and spirits are known as the three treasures; they represent the ability to transform from one state of being to another and form the basis of all inner alchemy.

THE THREE TREASURES

Jing, essence, is the most subtle form of material substance. It is the basis of physical life inherited from our mother and father, and in its most physical manifestation relates to sperm and ovum. It implies a form of matter so broken down that it is able to be rebuilt into any shape or pattern. The Chinese character 'jing' can also be used to mean light and subtle, and anything more subtle, more broken down would no longer be able to recreate form. The essences are considered to be within the realm of 'no form', but with the ability to create form. But the essences are not simply the basic building blocks of life – they also contain the coding necessary for its rebuilding. They contain the information that allows development and growth, and also the ability to rebuild the body according to its original pattern. This coding is inherited from our parents and according to the Chinese keeps intact the lineage of the ancestors.

If the meridians provide the energetic structure for the body, the essences weave the individual pattern. In weaving cloth the warp provides the vertical axis of stability, but in itself it is nothing but threads stretched between two poles. It is not until the threads of the weft intermingle with the warp that there is any cohesion, any structure, any wholeness. In much the same way the meridians create a potential structure for the body aligned to the axis of heaven and earth, but it is through the action of the essences that they are bound together to make the physical being. The meridians give the heavenly guideline, the essences weave the individual pattern.

Being of the earth, the essences, though subtle, are still material. Their natural tendency is to bind together. They move towards each other, much as sperm and ovum bind to make a new life. In chapter 8 of the Spiritual Axis, the Yellow Emperor asks his minister Qi bo to describe the unfolding of life. Qi bo describes the essences intertwined, embracing, suggesting that it is this embrace of essences that attracts spirit. The character used for this movement of the essences towards each other can also be translated as desire, possibly implying the sex drive, or simply the desire for life. As it is the interaction of the essences which takes the potential for life in general and creates an individual life, it is the spirits which are able to guide the individual life into the future. The essences hold the code for the development of the physical form and the elements of the psyche, but it is spirit which guides the unfolding of individual destiny.

The shen, or spirits, are our direct individual contact with heaven. They are able to keep us within the heavenly guidelines for our life and our development, helping us to grow, move on, transform. The shen are often likened to a flock of birds – the action of the essences the preparation of a nest. If the birds are able to find a suitable place to live, they will stay. Many meditation and exercise practices are aimed at providing this acceptable home for the spirits. Like birds, the spirits like calm; too much excitement is like shaking the tree and the birds will fly away. As we have seen, the Daoist classics tell us that in order to attract the spirits we must create an empty heart – not a heart that is empty of emotion and feeling, but a heart that enables emotions and feelings to flow freely, without clinging and without attachment. The empty space within our physical heart allows the constant filling and emptying, and it is this rhythmic pumping of the heart that drives the lifeforce. But the heart needs calm in order to maintain this regular rhythm, and a heart that is calm will be able to attract spirit. When we are agitated we create clouds of emotion which obscure us from spirit, as clouds obscure the sun. Creating a peaceful heart is the process of eliminating the clouds.

The shen, or spirits, as presented in the medical classics, do not merely affect our emotional and spiritual life, nor even our mental capacity; they are said to dwell in the heart and in the blood, and they are present, through the blood, at the level of our cells and with every circumstance of our daily life. The shen combine with the essences in order to make the intelligence of life; the essences giving identity and the information for physical structure, the shen bringing the inspiration for development. The double expression 'jingshen', essences/spirits, is commonly used in Chinese to denote the perfect mingling of heaven and earth within an individual, and we could possibly translate 'jingshen' as consciousness. The jingshen is seen in the shine in the eye, the glow of the complexion. In our analogy with weaving, the jingshen would be the beauty of the individual pattern, the subtle mix of colour and form; each individual thread combining in a complex mesh which, once complete, is able to present a single unity.

Qi is the mediator between the heavenly guidelines and the earthly structure. Everything that exists between heaven and earth is animated by qi. Qi is closely related to the breath, and in the human body our breath is certainly the most accessible illustration of qi, but qi is more than breath. It refers to respiration in its widest sense. In plant life, respiration implies the ways in which the plant makes energy. And within the human, cellular respiration is the only way that energy is produced within the organism. Similarly, qi is responsible for all exchanges, all movement, all energetic transformation. It represents the continual renewal of life, the dynamism of the lifeforce. Maybe it is less personal than essence and spirit, more of a universal movement. Within the body it is given different names according to its different

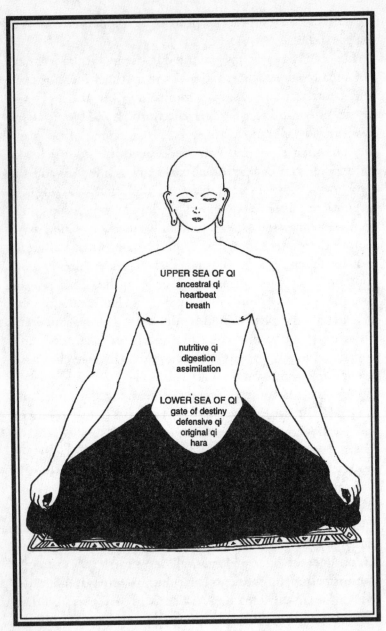

Plate 4

functions. At root, qi is always the same but in medicine it is differentiated so that we can talk about it and particularly so that we can discuss its pathology.

There are three types of qi which are said to have their origin in the lower, middle and upper parts of the body. In the lower abdomen our defensive qi (wei qi) is made from the coarser aspects of digested food. From the lower abdomen it rises to the chest where it begins its circulation throughout the body. It is said to be active at the interior by night, and at the exterior during the day. In the upper abdomen nutritive qi (ying qi) is active. This is produced from the more subtle essences of food and circulates in the various channels of communication, supplying essential nutrients to the cells of the body. In the chest is the ancestral qi (zong qi), sometimes called gathering qi. This is the qi responsible for the rhythmic beating of the heart and the inhalation and exhalation of the breath. It creates all circulations and cycles of regulation. This qi is the most light and subtle and is filtered by the action of the diaphragm. These three types of qi make up what are known in Chinese medicine as the three heaters, or the three burning spaces, which refers to the transformation of energy at these three different levels (Plate 4).

The qi gives movement, it sets things in motion, giving the strength and ability for growth and development. It moves the blood, allowing it to circulate well through the complex system of blood vessels. It holds things in place, giving direction and elasticity. It controls the liquids of the body, keeping them inside the body, allowing their diffusion to the skin, and their evacuation through the bladder. It controls digestion and assimilation, aiding the transformation of food and allowing the subtle aspects of food to be distributed to the appropriate part of the body, the less subtle to be transformed or eliminated.

Within the body there are two so-called seas of qi: one in the lower abdomen and one in the centre of the chest. The sea of qi in the abdomen is located a few inches below the navel, in Japanese it is known as the hara, and is the energy centre most commonly described in all martial arts and meditation practices in Japan. In Japanese medicine hara diagnosis forms an important part of treatment, as it is understood that the energy in the lower abdomen gives a clear indication of the general energy levels of the whole body. If the hara is strong, there is a good chance of recovery, if it is weak, recovery will be more difficult. The upper sea of qi is located on the midline between the breasts, and corresponds with the energy centre related to the heart. These two seas of qi are important in all Daoist exercise and meditations.

Essence, qi and spirit are present at every level of the body and in every act of transformation. But it is qi that we are able to work with — it is qi that we are able to influence. By working with our qi, we may make better use of our essences and provide a better home for the spirits. Many translations of Daoist alchemical writings refer to the refinement of essence to make qi and the refinement of qi to make spirit. But both the medical and Daoist classical texts are quite clear that essences are predetermined. They are of their very nature unalterable. The spirits come and go as they will, they cannot be made. But the essences can be enhanced by the qi, and through the qi there can be a good relationship between the essences and the spirits. And although the spirits cannot be made, they can be called, they can be attracted. So it is by working with the qi that we can aid the constant renewal of our physical bodies and attract the spirits to give our lives direction.

There is another type of qi which is called original or source (yuan) qi. It is related to the lower abdomen and what is called in many of the classic texts 'the movement of life between the kidneys'. This is the qi that we inherit at our birth, and its quality defines our constitution. It is the original qi that acts as a catalyst in all other transformations, facilitating each and every act of qi all over the body. The movement of life between the kidneys is also called the gate of destiny, which is the origin of the fire in the lower abdomen. It is here that all life is said to begin. It is here that the development of the channels of lifeforce occurs, it is from here that the life of the foetus has its origin. Through all its activities within the bodily systems, it is the original or source qi which keeps us in touch with the pattern of our origin and the blueprint of our future potential. It keeps us in touch with the fire of the gate of destiny which is the source of all change and transformation.

THE GATE OF DESTINY

Chinese art often shows the twin dragons of yin and yang intertwining to create the knot of life. Within the individual, this knot of life is called the gate of destiny. It is the place from which each individual human life is generated, and from which it continually draws its inspiration. It is both the origin of our own life and of our ability to produce another life. It is the source of all creativity and fertility, and the source of our constitutional energy, our original qi.

Original (yuan) can also be translated as 'principal', 'mysterious', 'source', and the gate of destiny is our connection with the undivided oneness that is beyond the duality of matter and energy, yin and yang. It is our connection with the undifferentiated chaos of life – the mystery. According to acupuncture theory, it is our connection to our constitutional energy and our informational coding. But as well as allowing the physical development of life, the gate of destiny passes on the code of our individual nature, it carries the blueprint for the unfolding of our lives on earth.

Some English translations prefer to use the phrase 'the gate of life', but although more acceptable to the Western mind, this is not an accurate translation. The etymology of the character for destiny (ming) suggests a 'heavenly mandate', but also 'proper nature' and 'that which is natural'. In a culture where we are used to seeing the divine as something apart from ourselves, and divine ordination as a force that is often opposing our own free will, it is difficult to imagine that our own true nature and divine ordination may be one and the same thing. But this is the meaning implied in the Chinese. In the West we are not comfortable with the concept of destiny. Destiny is often seen as belonging to the realm of fairground fortune-tellers and the kind of fatal-ism that is the opposite of self-responsibility and self-transformation. It carries a suggestion of the unavoidable. We could more accurately say that the gate of destiny is 'the gate of the unfolding of life according to my true nature'.

The Chinese character for heaven (tian) can also be translated as 'nature'. Looking at different translations of the *Dao de Jing*, for example, it is interesting to see that some translators prefer one translation, others another. This ability to see the divine as 'what is natural' is quite different from the Western tendency to oppose god and nature. In Chinese philosophy, heaven represents the movement of the stars, the moon, the sun; it represents cycles of change and transformation, illustrated by the movement of nature through the four seasons; birth and growth in the spring, flowering and bearing fruit in the summer, harvesting and cutting back in autumn and storing and conserving in winter. The first two chapters of the *Yellow Emperor's Inner Classic* tell us that in order to maintain our health we should live according to these cycles of heaven, modelling our own actions on those of nature, expanding when it is appropriate to expand, conserving when it is appropriate to conserve.

The importance of the gate of destiny in Chinese medicine is to remind us that we have a purpose in the world, a destiny to fulfil which, according to the ancient roots of the word, is none other than to discover our true nature. If we are able to realise our proper nature, the nature given to us by divine decree, or the mandate of heaven, we are able to become what the old Chinese texts call a 'real person'. Heaven, or the divine, is nothing other than the true nature of things. Following the Dao is nothing other than following the true nature of things, or living according to our true nature.

The profundity of this concept lies in the fact that the gate of destiny is not merely metaphysical speculation pertaining to the realm of mind and spirit, but the very centre of our ability to create physical energy, to continually recreate our own lives and also our ability to produce new life. The gate of destiny is the point from which life begins. From the state of undifferentiated oneness, it is the point of separation from which all manifestation occurs. At the gate of destiny there is the primal division into yin and yang, water and fire, matter and energy. It is the source and also the return.

According to the medical classics it is from here that 'all life explodes'. It is at the gate of destiny that the primal energy divides into yin and yang, creating the first of the energy channels, which from their origins at the knot of life move downwards and divide into the primary channels of yin and yang to make a circle around the body, the yang on the back, the yin on the front. Along these primary pathways the energy centres or chakras are located with their roots in the spinal column, their flowers on the front midline, each centre having its corresponding acupuncture points.

The network of channels and meridians which all have their origin at the gate of destiny provide pathways for the movement of information in the form of essence, spirit and qi. With the information from the gate of destiny as their guide, they continually adjust the form according to the original pattern. The deepest and most fundamental of these informational pathways are the eight extraordinary meridians. They are considered to be most active during foetal development, but give continual support to the twelve ordinary meridians during adult life, providing the basic pattern of information concerning structure and the primitive organisation of yin and yang. The twelve ordinary meridians become more active after birth, and are primarily concerned with the actions and interactions of the five elements and the internal organs.

This primary division of yin and yang at the gate of destiny is possibly a reflection of the first and continuing cell division which takes place during the early development of the foetus. It is interesting to see that in the first few days of development the cells multiply along a single axis, which eventually becomes the spinal cord. There are then a series of foldings which create more and more complexity within the developing organism. As the foetus grows, the primary yang impulse is seen in the spinal cord on the back, the primal yin impulse in the abdomen.

The primary yin and yang channels are responsible for the basic balance of yin and yang within the body. Their origin is deep within the belly and, when fully developed, they emerge and diverge within the perineum. The primary yang channel runs up the spinal column, over the top of the head, the primary yin channel up the front midline of the body. They meet again in the mouth. These two channels form the basis of most Chinese meditation practices, and we will look at them in greater detail as we progress (Plate 5).

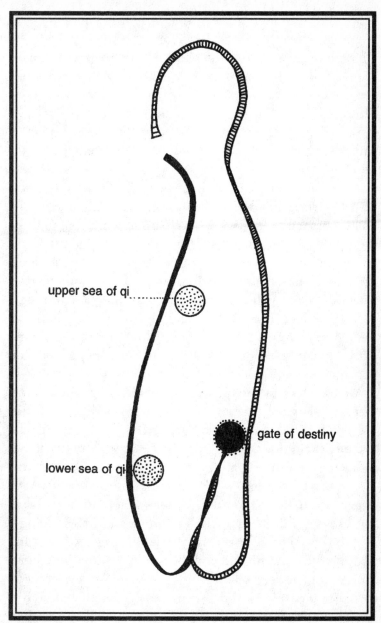

upper sea of qi

gate of destiny

lower sea of qi

Plate 5

A third channel gathers together the yin and yang potential to create a new burst of movement and life. In Chinese medical theory this third energy channel is linked with the development of the four limbs, as well as providing a connection between the sexual organs and the energy centre of the heart. Recent advances in embryology have shown that during the earlier stages of development a particular group of cells – sometimes referred to as 'the growing edge' – form the beginnings of the four limbs and aid the fusion of the front and the back of the body. They help to define growth and structure. Eventually these cells form a particular kind of sensitive tissue which is found in the hands, the feet, the genitals and around the mouth in the completed human form. All the tissue that is found along the 'ridge' has a particularly strong connection via the nervous system with the brain. The ridge also passes through the nipple line. It is very interesting to see that many of these diverse connections resemble those made by this third extraordinary meridian, known as the chong mai or penetrating vessel.

We have seen that in early embryological development the foetus undergoes a series of foldings around what is the precursor of the spinal column. As the original mass of cells extends along this vertical axis, the heart actually sits above the brain, the diaphragm on top of the heart. The heart is the first organ to develop and during the early stages it is the largest organ. It is almost as if its very weight makes it bend forwards towards the umbilicus in the first of these foldings. At the other end of this axis, the developing sexual organs fold upwards towards the umbilicus to a position just above the developing lower limbs. In each stage of development there is a balance of the increase of function and the necessary protection: a time of growth and a time of consolidation.

As we saw earlier with our brief look at numerology, odd numbers represent yang and the tendency to create new growth, the even numbers represent yin and the tendency to stabilise form and to extend protection. In accordance with this, the fourth of the extraordinary meridians brings the developing form a sense of volume and solidity. Being the only energy channel which has a lateral flow, it is described as enfolding the lower abdomen like a belt (Plate 6).

These four basic energy channels have a joint origin deep within the belly and create the fundamental structure of the individual form. The remaining four of the eight extraordinary meridians are responsible for the further balancing of yin and yang within the developing form. The first two create a circle in much the same way as the primary channels, but encompassing the whole body – beginning together at the heels and meeting again at the eyes. They are responsible for the constant exchange and interchange between yin and yang. The final pair are less to do with exchange and interaction, each having its own responsibility for organising the yin or the yang function – the yin function being active on the interior and the fluids of the body, the yang function being active at the exterior and particularly on the defensive energy. According to the *Yellow Emperor's Inner Classic*, 'Yin is on the interior, but it is yang that gives it action. Yang is on the exterior, but it is yin that maintains it there.'

Although much of our everyday energy production is taken over at birth by the twelve ordinary meridians, it is still the eight primary channels which are responsible for maintaining our basic patterns and keeping us in line with our true nature. It is these eight extraordinary meridians which form the basis of qi gong practice, and also of Daoist meditation. Working with these channels, we attempt to regain the symmetry lost through development and through illness, shock and trauma.

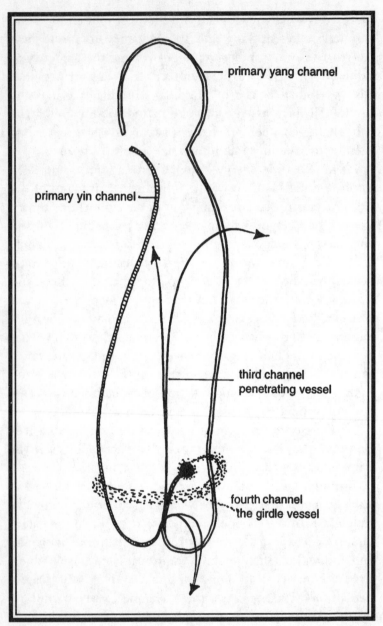

Plate 6

In many of the old alchemical texts the gate of destiny is portrayed as a cauldron where the fire (yang) is acting on the water (yin) to create a new and usable substance. Alchemy is nothing other than the speeding up of processes which are already at work in nature. In the attempt to turn base metals to gold, alchemists East and West attempted to exert fire and pressure to hurry along the processes which are at work deep within the earth. In the process of inner alchemy, the Daoist sages used the control of the breath and the stimulation of the fire of the gate of destiny to aid the transformation of energy.

Fire and water are the basic requirements of the alchemist. The process of energy production within the body is often compared in the medical classics to cooking a good meal: the adjustment of the flame under the cooking pot and the addition of the appropriate amount of liquid at just the right time is essential for the preparation of nutritious food. Chinese cooking aims to break down the raw ingredients sufficiently for the optimum extraction of energy. Cooked for too long the energy is lost; not long enough and it is difficult to assimilate; too much water and we have an indigestible soggy mess; too much heat and the food is burnt and dry. Similar expressions are used in medicine to explain the interactions of yin and yang, fire and water within the body, and particularly the way the body is able to transform food into energy: too little transforming fire and the body may tend to be sluggish, hold water, create phlegm, put on weight; too much heat and the fluids may be lost, the body unable to make flesh, the skin dry and the joints stiff.

The balance of yin and yang, fire and water, essence and spirit are at the heart of Chinese medicine, and form the basis of many of the traditional exercise and meditation techniques. Some aim to restore balance, others to aid the production of energy and the processes of transformation. Many exercises aim to reinstate the balance of yin and yang by directing the awareness to the primary yin and yang pathways. Others aim to keep the organism in touch with the fire of the gate of destiny by constant repetition of simple breathing exercises. The lower abdomen, the hara, the gate of destiny is considered important for physical health and stability, because it provides a connection to the origin. Being connected to the origin implies a connection to the way of heaven, being aligned to what is natural.

The Chinese medical classics contain much simple down to earth advice and wisdom on how to live our lives and how to align with our personal destiny. They paint a picture of our place in the cosmos which appeals to the imagination and can provide a useful map for our journey. They suggest that health is a process of continual change and adaptation. As the circumstances of life change it is necessary to let go of the past and move on. In order to remain healthy it is often necessary to let go of patterns of behaviour which are no longer relevant, to free the body of old habits which are no longer helpful to its continual process of becoming. Today, in the Western world, so many of our illnesses are a sickness of the soul; of a soul longing to fulfil its potential. In classical Chinese medicine good health automatically includes an acceptance of personal destiny; not so much a belief in fate as the need to fulfil one's purpose in life. The concept of destiny is closely connected to the Dao, the way or the path. It is the Dao as it relates to the individual, and each individual has his or her path to follow. Following your true path may not automatically lead to health and longevity, but failing to take destiny or the demands of your soul into consideration will most definitely lead to disease.

Soon after my thirtieth birthday, I returned to Japan from six months' travelling in India. My intention was to request the permission of my teacher to study with him further. I saw this as a kind of spiritual commitment and expected there to be some conditions to my acceptance. I will sweep floors, I thought, accept two years of celibacy – others before me had been given such tasks. But no. When we finally met up, the only instruction I received was, 'Be yourself.' I was young, and assumed that this meant I was still unworthy of the real work. Only now can I see it as the highest teaching. Over the following years the words remained with me. I played with them in my mind like a zen koan. It was the thread that I held on to throughout the process of falling apart and putting myself together again which took place with alarming speed over the next two years. I remember as the words were spoken experiencing some disappointment – but deep inside there was a sense of shock and recognition.

Being yourself is not always easy, especially for those of us who since childhood have been taught to be something other. In my struggle with this teaching in Japan I possibly made the mistake of looking for an intellectual solution. How can I be myself if I no longer know who I am, I wondered. But meanwhile I continued with my practice. It is not possible to find the self with the mind. It is only by letting go of mental fabrications that the soul can make itself known.

Both my daily practice and the acupuncture treatment that I received in Japan were concerned with transformation. The combination of Indian yoga and meditation, Daoist inner alchemy and the Buddhist practices of emptiness all came together to provide a tool for progress. While we worked on energising and harmonising the body, we also worked to let go with the mind. Coming closer to the true nature is a process of letting go, letting go with the mind, letting go with the emotions, letting go of the conditioning of the body.

CAUSES OF DISEASE

Within the Chinese medical tradition there are two main categories for the causes of disease, generally called internal and external causes. External causes are those which are seen to attack the body from the outside, and in the Chinese texts were usually categorised by the climates related to the five elements (wind, heat, damp, dryness, cold) but also included plagues, parasites, epidemics, etc. Resistance to this external attack was seen to be dependent on both the strength of the invasion and the strength of the internal defence mechanisms. Many of the old herbal texts, Eastern and Western, tend to concentrate on this kind of external attack. As primitive agricultural societies they shared a similar dependence on the land. Conditions were harsh and there was little protection from extremes of climate. The Western concept of the four elements and the four humours has led to the development of a very similar system, which forms the basis for much Western herbalism and folk medicine. Ancient agricultural communities were of necessity aware of the cycles of nature, and within Northern agricultural societies the changes of climate throughout the four seasons became the basis for much of the understanding of nature and, by extension, an understanding of the effects of nature on human beings.

Within both the Chinese five-element system and the Western four-element system a comparison of the action of climates and emotions has also been drawn. Within the Western model the water element is cold, damp and phlegmatic in nature, the earth element cold, dry and melancholic in nature, the air element hot and damp and sanguine, the fire element hot, dry and choleric. An excess of the water element tends towards slowness and sluggishness, the earth element pessimism and chilliness, the air element robustness and quick temper, the fire element nervousness and stress. Placed around a map of the year, the winter solstice would occur between water and earth, the summer solstice between air and fire; the autumn equinox between fire and earth, the spring equinox between water and air (Plate 7).

The Chinese model stresses the elements as movements and tendencies, but there are many similarities. In the ancient models the earth element was generally placed at the centre, and a similar square pattern formed with the remaining four elements; water corresponding to winter and cold and the emotion of fear, fire to summer, heat and the emotion of joy; wood corresponding to spring and wind and the emotion of anger, metal to autumn, dryness and the emotion of sadness or melancholy. These correspondences may seem fanciful, but they can be explained in terms of the energetic effect that each emotion has on the body. For example, sadness has been observed to cause the energy to contract. The Chinese character for sadness (bei) shows a restriction on the heart. It is a feeling of constriction and pressure which is felt in the chest. Within the Chinese model this element also has a resonance with the lungs and it is in the lungs that this kind of energetic action will be felt. Autumn is the time when the energy of the earth begins to contract after the expansion of the summer. It is a time of darkening nights, of mists and melancholy. The earth is literally drying out and conserving its energy for the winter months. As the organ in the body that most loves expansion, the lungs find this movement difficult and clinically it is easy to observe that the majority of chest problems occur at this time of the year.

Moving into winter, the energy descends further down into the depths of the earth. It is said that at the winter solstice heaven and earth have no communication, the yin has retreated into the earth, the yang to heaven. This descending movement of the energy within the body corresponds to the

43

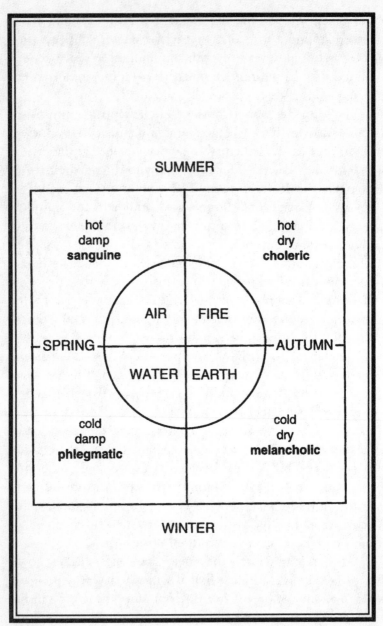

Plate 7

emotion of fear. And in the primitive societies within which these systems were evolved each winter there would have been a genuine fear for survival throughout the cold winter months. It is a time of consolidation and preservation, all the non-essentials having been stripped away in preparation for the descent into winter. Emotionally this is the descent into the underworld, the fear of the unknown – fears that when faced add to our wisdom.

This is a time for inner contemplation and meditation, preserving strength and energy. In primitive societies there would naturally be less activity in the winter. But working in a modern city we get very little idea of the cycle of the seasons and do not adjust our actions to the available energy in nature. Simply by going to bed a bit earlier in the winter we would begin balancing the energy according to the four seasons – which is seen as one of the most important steps to regain health in the ancient Chinese classics (Plate 8).

Chinese medicine often succeeds where orthodox medicine has failed by making very simple diagnosis according to the climates and seasons. Observing when patterns of an illness occur, whether they are better or worse from heat or cold, alleviated in the summer, or worse in damp weather, the practitioner is able to get closer to the cause of the problem. Asking what time of year the illness first occurred may be a clue to its origin. When treating arthritis, for example, the practitioner would use a different treatment depending on whether the arthritis was caused by cold, heat, damp or wind. Much of this kind of simple diagnosis is common sense and part of folk medicine in all traditions. It has been neglected by modern scientific medicine, as it does not fit into the current biomedical model.

Internal causes of disease are said to attack the body from within, and refer specifically to the emotions; each emotion

45

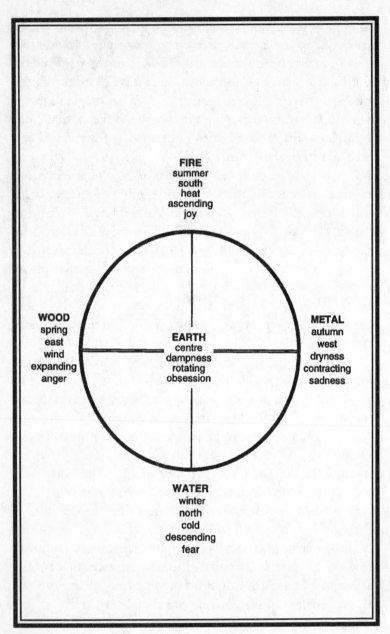

Plate 8

moving the qi, or energy, in a particular way. In health the emotions flow freely, moving through the energy system like wind through a willow tree, possibly shaking the leaves, but the root and trunk remaining untouched. It is only if emotions are suppressed or held on to for too long that imbalance occurs.

Working with the climates, the emotions and the corresponding effects on the bodily energy systems forms the basis for much of the clinical work of all Oriental medical professionals. We work in different ways and stress different aspects in our diagnosis, but at root it is much the same thing. This kind of treatment and diagnosis according to the pattern of the five elements and their corresponding emotions formed the basis of my book *Reclaiming the Wisdom of the Body* (Constable, 1997). But many of the health problems facing us in recent years seem to be so pervasive, affecting the organism at the deepest level of our being. This seems to be a level of imbalance which lies beyond these causes, beyond the balance of five elements and the treatment of individual organ systems. Many of the problems facing us today seem to suggest that the entire system is in a state of collapse. This became apparent in the 1980s with the rise of cases of AIDS and chronic fatigue syndrome – two clinical instances (one primarily external, one primarily internal) which suggest this kind of direct attack on the lifeforce.

In Chinese medicine, loss of sperm, the most material form of jing (essence), is said to lead to a diminution of the generative fire of the gate of destiny. This is the reason for many of the practices to control seminal emissions. The fire of the gate of destiny is also directly responsible for the transformation of defensive energy and the development of the immune system. Although AIDS is obviously an example of external attack, the susceptibility of sections of the gay community at the beginning of the epidemic could have some relation to this particular lack of resistance. Orthodox medicine has had little success in treating AIDS, possibly because at the level of lifeforce Western medicine has little to offer. It may also be the reason why those who have managed to survive against all medical odds have done so by addressing their emotional and spiritual as well as their physical needs.

Chronic fatigue syndrome, although on a different (i.e. non-life-threatening) level, causes just as deep a disturbance to the body/mind energies. In severe cases the sufferer may be unable to walk, unable to sleep, unable to think. Contrary to Victorian medical hypotheses of hysterical women and the still current tendency to think of sufferers as malingerers, the majority of cases that I have seen have been young, highly motivated individuals. The symptoms are pervasive, threatening all the bodily systems and especially those which are controlled by the autonomic nervous system, those deep unconscious rhythms of life that keep us inhaling and exhaling, breaking down and assimilating food, sleeping and waking; that keep our temperature regulated and our metabolism functioning. As well as consciously restoring rhythm to the breath, the most effective treatment in clinical practice is to strengthen the fire of the gate of destiny.

In many cases of chronic fatigue syndrome, the natural inhalation and exhalation of the breathing mechanism is hardly functioning. There may be long periods of time when there is hardly any breathing taking place, or the breath is so shallow that very little oxygen will be absorbed.

Within the most severe cases of chronic fatigue syndrome, two common patterns have emerged within my clinical practice: young men who have been unable to negotiate puberty successfully, and women who have been through some kind of sexual harassment and trauma. Underlying these two examples may be individual cases of childhood sexual abuse. In both cases there has been an unconscious denial of the sexual function, and a neglect of the energies of the gate of life to the extent that the original fire has all but gone out. No longer being able to transform and transmute, this lack of original qi manifests itself in the inability to take nourishment from food, the inability to take energy (oxygen) from the breath, and often, significantly, in the inability to keep the lower body warm. The inability to take nourishment from food may materialise in two ways. Either there is an accumulation of weight due to the deposit within the tissues of untransformed matter, or the nutrients are excreted from the body without being absorbed. The process of transformation of matter from one state (food) to another (usable energy) is unable to take place. Where there is weight gain, in some cases this may be very obviously below the waist so that the legs and hips are proportionally larger than the top of the body. The area below the waist is often described as feeling dead or cold or even numb, although these feelings may be deeply hidden and not emerge until some degree of strengthening has occurred.

If the metabolic type is such that the nutrition from food is unable to be absorbed, the individual may become more and more emaciated, more and more ethereal. Both conditions are a separation of yin and yang: in one case the body becoming more of the earth, but unenergised by the transforming fire of yang; in the second case there is less and less yin, and without the stability of the earth, the energy of fire and heaven is unable to manifest itself. In cases of anorexia there may be such a resistance to the material that a totally distorted sense of reality emerges, until the body is actually incapable of taking nourishment. These are extremes, but they serve to illustrate patterns which we all experience in varying degrees, patterns which are becoming more and more common.

If the physical and emotional trauma that we all experience throughout our lives are left unaddressed, a state of imbalance may arise which eventually becomes illness. We all develop illness patterns which tend to repeat themselves, creating grooves of habitual action and reaction. Old injuries leave us with areas of weakness, which we tend to protect, or under-use, and emotional traumas may keep us trapped in old patterns of behaviour, even though the pattern no longer provides any support. It is by addressing these destructive patterns of behaviour that we are able to regain our centre and our stability. By remaining true to our centre we are able to change and flow with the circumstances that face us.

Many experienced alternative practitioners see illness as a digression from the pattern of the origin, and their work as guiding the individual back to their own centre, their own symmetry. This may be structurally, by rebalancing the body through manipulation of the muscles and bones, or energetically, working with the hands or with acupuncture needles. It may be by working directly with emotional states in order to free energetic blockage and restore balance. We can imagine the body as a sphere, the energy lines forming a surface pattern much as the meridians of the globe. Our life experience tends to push us out of shape – each accident, each operation, each emotional trauma denting us in one way or another. What we need is to become whole again. We cannot turn back the clock, we cannot replace those lost organs, erase those scars – whether physical, mental or emotional – but we can work with our energy to create a new wholeness. And in realigning with our original pattern, we can recoup our strength and move on.

Occasionally, imbalance within the system may be a

necessary stage on the way to a new level of being, and what we see as illness may sometimes be a necessary part of growth. Working with energy we can allow the body to realign without suppression. Working with energy will give the body a chance to find its own equilibrium, and meanwhile we are able to slow down, take stock of our lives and, if possible, realign with our personal life path. Much of modern drug-based medicine aims to alleviate symptoms and, in the process, very often suppresses the cause of the problem. The symptoms may or may not be cured, but unless we are able to address the cause, the problem will doubtless reappear on the same or possibly at a deeper level. If the imbalance is merely suppressed the chance for transformation is lost.

There are many practices and therapies which claim to invigorate the process of transformation and to enhance both our physical and spiritual well-being. Yoga, tai ji, qi gong, acupuncture and shiatsu massage in particular work directly with the subtle energy of the body in order to bring about change. Because subtle energy is an intermediary between the physical, mental and emotional aspects of our being, working with energy is effective on all of those levels. By working with qi we can transmute matter to energy, energy to matter; with exercise we can realign and re-establish communication with our inherited patterns. With meditation we can reconnect with our source.

Although the concepts of Oriental medicine are profound and sometimes difficult to grasp, the methods are almost shockingly simple; so simple in fact that we often ignore them in favour of a more sophisticated approach. But to the Oriental mind it is the repetition of simple tasks that create change. Water continually running over stone will eventually wear it away, and it is the repetition of simple techniques that often brings about the most profound change. In the old

Daoist texts breathing exercises were likened to the continual ploughing of a field, the repetition of the same action over and over again eventually bringing about the required conditions for growth and change. The aim of many of these exercises is to restore the body to its original state of harmony, and to strengthen the connection to the gate of destiny; to assist with the natural process of energy production, generation and refinement and, in doing so, to assist the unfolding of the individual destiny – the future which is already within us.

DAOIST ALCHEMY AND THE THREE CINNABAR FIELDS

I had always been drawn to Zen Buddhism, and when I first arrived in Japan after travelling throughout Asia it was the study of Zen that was foremost in my mind. I was therefore surprised that it was the Shinto shrines which captured my imagination, and when I eventually committed myself to serious study, it was with a Shinto priest, not a Zen master, as I had perhaps expected. But in Japan traditions are often mixed, and boundaries easily crossed. Most families observe both Buddhist and Shinto rites, and within the Zen tradition especially there are many correspondences. The Chinese roots of Zen (Cha'an) are said to draw heavily on Daoism, and Shinto has many similarities with Daoism, in embracing the philosophy of yin and yang, and in its assertion that spirit exists in everything. Much of its symbolism is strictly Japanese, but much is shared also with Daoism. 'Shin' is the Japanese transliteration of the Chinese ideogram 'shen' (spirit), 'to' the Japanese equivalent of 'Dao'. Shinto is therefore literally 'the way of the spirits'.

My training in Japan was eclectic and my teacher drew on Indian yoga, Japanese Buddhist and Chinese Daoist practices. He used what he knew from his experience to be most effective, and gave each of his students a practice suited to his or her individual needs. But the one practice that seemed to be common to all students was the Daoist meditation called the circulation of light, or turning the light around. Drawing on the Chinese vision of energy circulation within the primary yin and yang channels, this was the prerequisite for all other practice. This was the basic meditation to calm the nervous system, regulate the energy channels and balance yin and yang. As a simple meditation practice it involved the visualisation of a light, travelling up the spine, over the top of the head to the point between the eyebrows, and down the front midline of the body, through the heart and the lower abdomen, to complete the circle in the perineum.

This circulation of light is the basis of all Daoist meditation practices, and the focus of many of the later Daoist alchemical writings. The practice is traditionally illustrated by symbolic diagrams which portray the body as a landscape. The Chinese medical tradition draws many comparisons between the movement of fluids and energy in the body with the movement of water over the earth. In much the same way as the flow of water over the earth shapes and forms the contours of the landscape, so the flow of energy within the body both creates and maintains its shape. The early Daoist seers explored the inner landscape of the body with a fervour equal to their counterparts in the physical world. They described their journey in a language that was deliberately symbolic and obscure and Daoist alchemy remained a closed and secret method for many centuries. Daoist inner alchemy is the practice of meditation and breathing techniques to enhance the natural transformation processes at work within the body. Working with the three treasures – essence, qi and spirit – these practices are seen as an aid to health by strengthening the transformative function of the qi, and a way back to the true nature by aligning the spirit and essence.

With the aid of one of these body maps, we will follow the circulation of the primary yang and primary yin channels in the body and gain some understanding of the subtle energetics at work. It is my hope to explain some of the more obscure symbolism surrounding this subject, but those who are not interested in delving more deeply into obscure Chinese symbolism, should feel free to skip this part, come back to it later or not at all. This depth of information is by no means essential to benefit from the practice and the main points will be taken up again in the practical section of the book. Some may find the information fascinating, others may find it confusing. And it is important to remember that this is only one of many possible interpretations. When attempting any kind of explanation of this kind, I am aware of the limitation of my knowledge. But I am also aware of the limitations of many other attempts and hope, for those interested in further study of this subject, the following ideas may find their place in the whole. Many of the explanations I have read about the symbolism of the circulation of light have been made by scholars unfamiliar with the Chinese medical texts, and particularly with the names of the acupuncture points. Many references are made to obscure palaces, halls and caverns which are the precise locations of acupuncture points on the primary yin and yang channels. When instruction of this kind has been obscured over the centuries, it is impossible to find one truth. And maybe that is the intention. We get from our search what we bring to it. But it is the experience within the body rather than within the mind that is important.

Those familiar with the Indian chakra system will be able to draw many parallels as we work our way around the body and we will discuss these connections in more detail in the following sections. It has been suggested, both in the traditional Indian system of chakras and nadis, and through the work of many modern healers, that the channels of subtle energy in the body are in some way a link or intermediary stage between the gross physical and the emotional body, and that the energy centres enable energy from one dimension to transform into another. In all subtle energy systems the spine is the major focus of this transformative work. In the Indian yoga tradition, the chakras are said to have their roots in the spinal column, their flowers on the front midline. Many of the points in acupuncture would suggest a similar correspondence. Let us explore these ancient maps of the body, with their obscure symbolism and see what light they can throw on our own understanding. It has been my experience that the rational mind finds it difficult to cope with such imagery, but that the intuition and bodily instincts understand well. If we try too hard to understand, we often miss the point. This kind of information needs to flow over us, to seep in gradually. The Chinese chose to use imagery and poetic descriptions for just this reason. Our problem is that we have no language, no place in our vocabulary to understand the mind/body relationships that are expressed here.

The most extraordinary and possibly the most difficult thing to grasp about the description of the energy body in the Chinese language is that it makes no distinction between the physical, the mental and the emotional. An acupuncture point translated as 'Long and Strong', suggesting the great concentration of grounding strength in the area of the base of the spine, may refer as much to an emotional or mental as to a physical strength. Similarly, a point on the head denoting clarity will refer to mental clarity as well as to a physical clarity of the eyes or ears. We see the same idea reflected in the classical descriptions of the chakras. A weakness in the physical will automatically suggest a weakness in the mental and emotional aspects of our being, not just through cause and effect, but just because there simply cannot be one without the other.

The Inner Body Map (Plate 9)

The illustration that we are using here is a drawing based on the Tang Dynasty inner body diagram, originating from the eighth century AD. A similar map can be found today on a stone tablet in the White Cloud monastery in Beijing. A coloured version on silk also exists in the Imperial Palace in the Forbidden City. It is very likely that by the eighth century AD there had been much exchange of ideas between India and China, and that the Indian understanding of the chakras had made an impact on the Daoist methods of meditation, but the Daoist body map remains essentially Chinese. It shows the trunk of the body depicted as a landscape, and though vague in form, it is quite possible to distinguish the form of a person sitting in meditation. In various parts of the body there are images from nature, particularly rocks which tend to represent the bodily structure and water, which represents the flow of energy. The journey described is a journey up the primary yang channel from the base of the spine over the top of the head to the mouth, and down the primary yin channel, from the mouth, through the throat and down into the belly. As we follow the imagery in the Daoist body map and look at some of the acupuncture points along the way, try to let go of some assumptions we tend to hold about the body. Begin to see the body as an energy field full of potential for change and transformation. Remember that the meridian system is our guide to wholeness, and by visualising our wholeness we can begin to heal.

The starting point and the ending point of the journey is the belly – the place of our original qi. It is at this place deep within the lower abdomen that the three primary energy channels (the primary yin channel, the primary yang channel and the penetrating vessel – the first three of the eight

Plate 9

extraordinary meridians) have their joint origin. From here they descend into the perineum, the yang channel surfacing midway between the anus and the coccyx, before surging upwards through the spinal column. In the lowest part of the diagram we can see water lapping over rocks; the rocks symbolising the bones of the pelvis and sacrum, the water the as yet undifferentiated flow of the three primary channels. At the very base of the spine there is a water wheel, with two young children working hard to turn the flow of energy. This is the point of differentiation – the yin energy accumulating at the base, the yang energy turning to rise up through the spinal column towards the brain. The two children treading the water wheel are one male, one female, representing the balance of yin and yang. Their youth represents the purity of mind necessary for the serious undertaking of Daoist alchemy, and the aim to restore the form to its original child-like symmetry. The water wheel symbolises the strength and force needed to create this upward movement through the spinal cord. The movement of energy through the spinal column is likened to a hydraulic system of canals and irrigation channels, and the journey is punctuated by various gates, as the energy negotiates particularly hazardous obstacles in its ascent. Each gate represents a stage of the journey and symbolises a refinement of energy. Blockages at any level will be due to an accumulation of physical, mental and emotional debris – the continual circulation of the breath is the broom we use to clear the channel. The exercise is therefore both diagnostic and therapeutic.

The acupuncture point between the anus and the coccyx, the first point of the primary yang channel, is called Long and Strong (qiang liang). Its name suggests a great force of strength. The Chinese character 'qiang' contains the image of the archer's bow, with all the dynamic tension needed to project the arrow to meet its target. It is the strength accumulated at the base of the body which allows the energy to surge into the spinal channel and reach the head, bringing clarity and possibly enlightenment. In the diagram it is labelled 'North Sea water flows in reverse to reach the summit of the Southern Mountains' and it is this initial push of the water wheel which begins the circulation through the primary yang channel. This is called the first gate, the gate of immortality.

Once through the wheel, the water moves up through the spinal channel, passing slabs of rock which represent the sacrum and the lower lumbar vertebrae; it then meets with the alchemical cauldron, and the fire of the gate of destiny. Here the interaction of fire and water creates vapours in the first refinement of energy. Above the fiery cauldron is the radiance of the supreme ultimate (tai ji), the connection with the origin. In the inscription on the stone tablet this is the 'gateway to the origin', the 'crossing of the energy of heaven and earth'. It is the place where the energies of heaven and the energies of earth first manifest themselves within the body. The dynamic balance of yin and yang is represented by the four tai ji symbols.

The names of the acupuncture points in this area are the yang pass (yang guan) located between the fourth and fifth lumbar vertebra, the gate of destiny (ming men) between the second and third lumbar vertebra and the suspended pivot (xuan shu) between the first and second lumbar vertebra. Xuan shu has an alternate meaning of suspended above the void, or to be suspended by heaven. It suggests a kind of ease of movement when one is suspended by heaven and in touch with the true nature of things. It is an ease of movement which can apply as much to physical movement and the articulations of the spinal column, which are all seen as pivoting in suspension, or to the ease in which we are able to move through life. Most acupuncture point names, and in fact many Chinese descriptions in general, will imply many levels of interpretation by the juxtaposition of characters. Located as it is directly above the gate of destiny, the suspended pivot suggests the ease and agility with which we are able to live once aligned with our true nature.

The third gate is at the level of the heart. The acupuncture points in this area of the spine are absolute yang (zhi yang), the spirit watchtower (ling tai) and the spirit path (shen dao). Absolute yang, located between the seventh and eighth thoracic vertebra, is at the same level as the so called 'yu', or control points, of the diaphragm. Within the acupuncture tradition it is only the rarefied energies that are able to pass through the filter of the diaphragm to enter the chest. The heart and lungs require the most pure and subtle of qi in order to function well. Absolute yang, or perfect yang, refers to the purity and clarity of the energy at this level.

With ling tai (between the sixth and seventh thoracic vertebra) we have the first allusion to spirit. Ling tai is a platform that was built to make offerings to the spirits, or an elevated tower constructed to bring us in closer contact with the energies of heaven. 'Ling' refers to the beneficial effect of the spirits. In the Han Dynasty, ling tai was the name given to a group of towers built by the Emperor. They were placed in such a way that he could survey the kingdom in each direction but also watch the stars. It was a place of observation, a place to receive information but also the place to be in touch with heaven. Observation of the heavens also suggests that the Emperor was in touch with the natural flow of time, able to act at the correct moment, and to perform the correct rituals according to the calendar.

The spirit path or the way of spirit is the name of the acupuncture point located between the fifth and sixth thoracic vertebra. This is shen dao, or the Japanese shinto, the way of the spirits, and it refers to the ability to conduct life according to the inspiration or guidance of heaven, because of the free communication with the spirits of the heart. This area of the spine is often an area of blockage and muscle tension. Tension in this area will often mean that the diaphragm does not work well, the breath becomes shallow, and eventually there will be a lack of clear yang energy to the brain which may result in headaches or unclear thoughts and vision. It is important to work both physically, with exercise, and energetically, with inner concentration, to free this gate and allow the refined yang energy access to the area of the heart and lungs. This area of the spine is connected to the heart centre, the middle dan tian, the middle field of cinnabar.

In some schools of Daoism, shen dao is the name given to a particular kind of divination by the stars. On Plate 9, in front of this gate we can see the spiral of the heart centre, the middle cinnabar field, and a representation of the constellation of the plough, the big dipper, pointing to the pole star over the crown of the head. We will see the great importance attached to this constellation as we progress.

Above the third gate the prominent vertebrae of the upper thoracics are represented as the jutting rocks of a pass. The primary yang channel then penetrates into the cavity of the skull, which is the location of the final gate. This is the area of the hind brain, the primitive brain. And it is this area that is worked on by cranial therapists who contact the subtle movement of the cerebrospinal fluids, often with profound results on the entire energetic system, and particularly on the nervous system and the brain. The acupuncture points at this level of the primary yang channel are the gate of the mute and the wind palace. The gate of the mute (ya men) is located an inch below the base of the occipital crest, and refers to a relationship with the tongue and to the heart, which can be seen on the diagram in the form of a twelve-storeyed pagoda. In Chinese medicine the tongue and speech are linked with the heart, and this point is classically used for all kinds of speech problems, particularly through shock, or an absence of the spirits of the heart, leading to muddled thinking and loss of clarity.

The wind palace (feng fu) is directly below the occipital protruberance and is seen similarly as a passage for the yang to enter the brain – the yang energy often being likened to the wind. Being a place of great influence, it is also a place of possible danger, and 'external attack', particularly from wind or cold, must be prevented at this vulnerable area. Traditionally it would be protected in much the same way as the fire of the gate of destiny must be kept warm and alive. The arrival of the clear yang to the brain brings clarity to the mind and to the upper orifices. It allows us to see clearly, to think clearly, to distinguish sounds and to differentiate smells and tastes. The qi gong exercise called heavenly drumming activates this area and keeps the energy moving.

At the top of the head are the nine peaks of the Kun Lun mountains, the legendary mountains of the south. These are the mountains of immortality, the dwelling place of the immortals, which rise up to heaven. Within Chinese numerology, nine is the number of completion. Hidden within the mountains is the palace of the mud pill - or the so-called elixir of immortality, and the original cavity of the spirit. This is the internal manifestation of the brow centre, the third elixir field, which corresponds to the pineal gland.

The acupuncture point at the top of the head is called one hundred meetings (bai hui), and either side of this point are two points of the bladder meridian called free communication with heaven (tong tian). In the baby this area is the fontanel which remains open in infancy until the spirit is settled. Many Daoist illustrations show the soul leaving the body through the top of the head, and in the Far East it is traditionally thought that the soul of the small child comes and goes until it finally is ready to settle in the body. It is at this the highest point of the head that the energy must be drawn back down. The primary yang channel descends over the forehead to the centre between the eyebrows, finally coming to rest within the mouth. Having reached its summit at the top of the head the energetic impetus continues in a natural completion like the curling of a whip.

The Upper Cinnabar Field

The centre between the eyebrows is the upper cinnabar field. Cinnabar, or sulphide of mercury, is the symbol of the alchemical process of transmutation; mercury representing the fluidity and coldness of yin, sulphur the fiery transforming power of yang. During the early centuries AD Daoist alchemists searched for the so-called 'elixir of immortality'. Some knew the substance to be something within themselves and worked with the awareness and the breath; others looked in the outside world, literally searching for the pill of immortality. The Chinese have always maintained a tradition of searching for substances in the plant, mineral and animal kingdoms to enhance their vitality. Cinnabar or sulphide of mercury became the symbol of this search. The inner alchemists saw this substance as the external symbol of the alchemical process of transmutation. Many followers of the schools of external alchemy – searching for a drug or pill that would give immortality – died in their search, many of mercury poisoning. The cinnabar fields or dan tian are the three centres of energy transformation. In Plate 9 it is represented by the black dot which is called the red sun. This is the radiance of our innate nature, our inner witness. It represents full consciousness, and its acupuncture point is called the hall of illumination (ming tang). The illuminated third eye is able to see past and future, to give inner sight and guidance. It is beyond the polarity of yin and yang, the place of detachment, of the impartial observer. This is the centre of the higher self, the inner voice of wisdom. Behind the red sun, Lao zi sits in meditation.

If you allow yourself to become silent and slowly bring the attention to the lower, the middle and finally the upper dan tian you will feel with this third centre a sense of withdrawal from the body, a quietening, a sense of detachment. The first two centres express the yin/yang, water/fire polarities and are vital to the stability of all the organs, both their yin/yang balance and their five-element resonances. This third centre is outside the five elements, outside the yin/yang polarity. We are no longer in the realm of medicine with its constant attempt to balance and harmonise. Here in this centre, yin and yang are one.

This idea is expressed in the Indian system with the concept that the eyebrow centre or ajna chakra is above karma. It is called the centre of control and command and refers to the ability to be in total control of oneself, and to take command of oneself. Its Sanskrit name 'ajna' has similarities with the Chinese character 'du' of the primary yang channel – the governor vessel. It is the ability to command and be in control, to oversee the workings of the body and the spirit. Many Indian systems of yoga suggest concentration to this centre as the safest, most reliable way to make spiritual progress.

Traditionally the centre of wisdom, it is often called the third eye. This third eye gives spiritual sight and insight and it represents the development of discriminating wisdom which is able to guide us to full self-responsibility. The third eye is referred to in many traditions and is thought by some to be the vestigial eye, the residual organ of guidance for migration, orientation and movement through life; sensitive to changing light and vibration, possibly to magnetism and energetic changes in the environment. Indian literature links this centre with the pineal gland, and modern research would suggest that the pineal gland may have such a function, though as yet its functions are not fully understood.

The red yang sun in the diagram is balanced by the yin moon located within the occipital crest. From the moon comes a clear liquid collected from the peaks of the mountains which pours down into the heavenly pond. It is called the dew from heaven, and it is collected in the back of the throat and brought down through the yin primary channel. Over the pool is the magpie bridge which represents the tongue. When curled back and allowed to rest naturally on the roof of the mouth, the tongue creates the bridge between yin and yang, the end of the primary yang channel and the beginning of the primary yin channel. In this position the tongue is relaxed, the throat is relaxed, words cannot be formed and the mind becomes calm. Here we have the image of water as a calm still pond, mirroring heaven: no longer the yang aspect of water as a dynamic force – the raging torrent within the ravine – but the calm still pool, bringing reflection, calm and inner nourishment.

The heavenly pool is the name given to the centre of the Chinese compass used in feng shui, and suggests a place of calm and emptiness from which all emerges.

A second figure in this upper part of the diagram stands beside the magpie bridge. This is the figure of the jade-eyed barbarian monk, usually thought to be Bodhidharma, the Indian Buddhist monk who travelled to China from Southern India. He stands on the ground, his arms upstretched to heaven. He was known as 'the friend of the Dao', and founded Chan Buddhism, later to be called Zen in Japan. The inscription on the painting reads 'The jade-eyed barbarian monk holds the heavens in his hands'. He is instructed to turn his gaze downwards to the lower abdomen, where he reappears in the form of the cowherd ploughing the lower field of cinnabar. Within the Zen tradition much emphasis is placed on the lower abdomen; breathing techniques and meditation practices focus on this area, known in Japanese as the hara. Zen teaches that one should remain focused on the body, focused on reality, rather than escaping into fantasy. Bodhidharma helps to focus the attention back to the body, emphasising that the aim of spiritual awakening is not escape, but the transformation of the matter.

Below the magpie bridge the twelve-storeyed pagoda leads downwards towards the heart. We are now following the pathway of the primary yin channel, and the acupuncture points in this area reflect the watery, yin nature of the pathway: receiver of fluids (cheng jiang), high spring (lian quan) are points on the chin and top of the throat.

The Middle Cinnabar Field

Standing on the spiral of millet seeds at the level of the heart is a figure called the divine boy stonecutter. He represents the true alchemist who has successfully turned base metal into gold. He is seen tossing gold coins into the air which form the constellation of the plough, or the big dipper. This constellation had a deep significance to the ancient Chinese, as it points the way to the pole star, the centre of the universe from which all life is suspended; from which all life comes and to which all life returns. In the diagram the plough points to the red pearl of immortality placed above the top of the head. This red pearl represents the transformed and immortal body of the perfected being.

In the practice of tai ji and qi gong the pole star is given much significance. Tai ji is one of the names given to this star – the great ridgepole or the supreme ultimate of the universe, around which all the constellations appear to rotate.

If you spend several hours watching a clear starry sky, attention fixed on the pole star, you become aware of the rotation of the earth, of the relationship between the earth and the heavens, and a relationship to this fixed point in the sky. The pole star seems to exert a pull, an antigravitational force. Alignment with the pole star is the starting point for tai ji, qi gong and much Daoist meditation practice. In tai ji classes the teacher often asks students to imagine that they are suspended by a thread which is attached to the centre of the top of the head and runs down the spinal column. The thread continues up to the pole star and is our connection with heaven, our source of yang. If we sit in meditation or stand in a qi gong pose imagining that the top of our head is connected to the pole star, our body becomes weightless, we are literally suspended from heaven.

In the Chinese classics, the Emperor is often given the name of the pole star. It is said that though he appears to do nothing, everything revolves around him. The spiral of millet seeds which we see within the heart centre in the diagram is the seal of the Emperor and is often seen as a design on regal garments. In Chinese medicine the heart is the Emperor, the centre which must be still and quiet for all movement to take place through it. It is the centre of the emotional life and, as such, must remain still and unperturbed. With a quiet heart, emotions come and go but are unable to disturb the stability at the centre. The seven stars of the plough also represent the seven emotions which flow through the heart: joy, anger, sadness, grief, worry, fear and fright. If they are freely expressed at the appropriate time emotions are a sign of life and health. It is only if they are suppressed or indulged that they will cause problems, beginning with an energetic imbalance which, if continued, may lead to physical or organic disease. A calm heart is the prerequisite for health. As the Emperor in the body, the heart is central to the inter-relationships of all the internal organs. It controls the blood, which carries oxygen and nutrition to all the cells of the body. But the blood also carries the shen, the spirit, which brings consciousness and intelligence to the cells. The heart beat and the blood are our symbols of life.

The acupuncture points in the area of the heart are the purple palace (zi gong), jade hall (yu tang) and central chamber (tan zhong). This is the middle cinnabar field, and the heart is the mediator between heaven and earth.

Next we come to the image of the weaving maiden, her spinning wheel again representing the circular energy of change and transformation. She is sitting in a grove of mulberry trees, spinning a silk thread which leads up to the spine above the gate of the heart. She is located at the middle heater and represents the extraction of energy from food. The thread represents the most subtle of the tastes which are able to diffuse themselves into the upper heater. As a woman she symbolises the nutritive aspect of yin.

The Lower Cinnabar Field

In front of the gate of destiny a cowherd ploughs the earth with an ox. The ploughing represents the continual repetition of simple movements to transform the soil, the ox is the animal connected to the earth element and represents stability and hard work. The writing on the stone tablet says:

In my house I plough my own field
In it are the spiritual shoots that can live ten thousand
  years.
The blossom is like yellow gold, and the colour changes,
The seed is like grains of jade and fruit is all around.
The planting here is based solely on the earth of the mid-
  dle castle

And the watering depends solely on the source of the Supreme Valley.

This is the field of elixir, the lower cinnabar field, the lower dan tian. The energy centre in the lower abdomen is the lower field of transformation. Ploughing the field represents the constant repetition of breathing exercises. The constant work of the plough produces a harvest of gold discs, which are then transferred to the heart (Plate 10).

Within the body this lower energy centre creates stability, solidity, grounding. The body's natural centre of gravity is just below the navel, which is also the centre of the body's electromagnetic fields. If we are able to centre our energy at this point in both exercise and meditation practice we are able to sit or stand for a long time without feeling tired. By focusing the breath and centring the mind on this energy centre, the body becomes stable, the vitality increased.

The acupuncture points in this area are the sea of qi (qi hai), the stone gate (shi men) and the gateway to the origin (guan yuan). They are located respectively one and a half, two and three inches below the navel. Qi hai is also called the lower sea of qi, the upper sea of qi being an alternative name for the point at the centre of the chest. These three points in the lower abdomen are the centre of concentration for many meditation and martial arts practices in the Far East. Breathing from the lower abdomen, actively using the diaphragm to increase the lung capacity, leads to the storage of energy in the hara. In Japan images of Bodhidharma portray him with a huge belly to illustrate his ability to accumulate energy in the lower dan tian. Little wooden dolls of Bodhidharma are given to children, and have their centre of gravity placed in such a way that however you may knock them over they always right

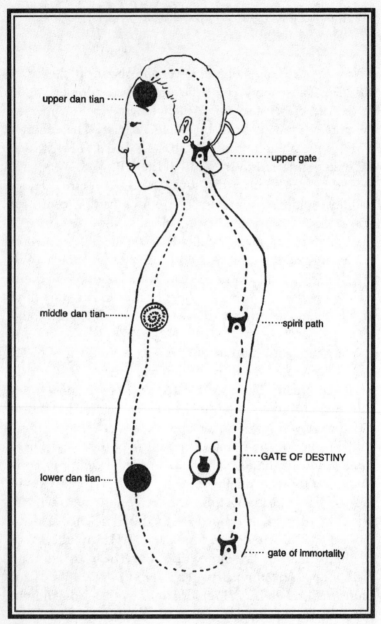

Plate 10

themselves. This is said to represent the stability that comes when you are centred in the hara or lower dan tian.

The lower dan tian is the centre of physical strength and the root of energy. Focusing here ensures a rooting in the earth and a grounding in reality. In Japan, Zen practitioners sit with their eyes only half closed, as a constant reminder that they are in the physical world, and should not get caught up in fantasy or imagination. The energies of the lower centre represent the lifeforce which needs to be tamed and used for progress.

The ten ox-herding or bull-herding pictures commonly used in Zen teaching illustrate the gradual disciplinary processes of Zen training, as man searches for his lower nature and his over-active mind, represented by the bull. Gradually he gets to know it and finally tames it. Pictures of Lao zi riding the bull are a sign that he has conquered his animal nature and brought his wandering mind under control. Zen goes further and suggests that ultimately the instinctive nature is completely reconciled and integrated until neither man nor bull exist. The bull is often depicted as gradually changing from black to white, showing how the mind is gradually moving from ignorance to enlightenment.

Here in the lower abdomen we complete the circle. Through the gateway to the origin, we return to our beginning point deep within the belly. By using the breath and allowing the imagination to create the circulation of light, we can regulate the yin and yang channels. By concentration on the lower, middle or upper dan tian, we can redress imbalances and remove blockages. A commentry on the illustration goes as follows:

The iron bull tills the ground so that the golden coins can
  be planted.
The stone-carving child strings them together.

In one piece of rice the world is hiding,
In a small pot can be cooked all the mountains and rivers.
The white-headed old man's eyebrows reach down to the
ground.
The jade-eyed barbarian monk holds the heavens in his
hands.
If you understand this mystery, then outside this mystery
there is no more mystery.
Inhalation and exhalation is the expansion and contrac-
tion of universe.
If you can intuitively perceive the meaning of this chart
You may know more than half the great way of the gold-
en elixir.

The inner landscape of the Daoist body map serves as a useful guide to Daoist inner alchemy and the three energy centres. It reflects the early Chinese view that mankind lives by the intermingling of the energies of heaven and earth. By tracing the energy back to its root, the Daoist seers attempted to return to their origin, to experience the one unity behind the diversity of earthly life.

In order to understand what is going on in our bodies and in our lives we need to enhance our ability to see behind – to see behind the external manifestation to the energetic workings within. We need to train ourselves to observe the external world in such a way that it reveals its inner secrets. We can begin to do this by looking within, by going on an inner journey, using the maps of those who have made similar journeys many times before. The maps are made obscure so that only those who persevere can penetrate their secrets.

Part Two
The Indian System of Chakras and Nadis

To be perpetually reborn is the condition of material immortality.

Sri Aurobindo

When I was studying in Japan, my teacher, Dr Hiroshi Motoyama, was conducting scientific research to verify the acupuncture meridian system, and making comparisons with the Indian system of chakras and nadis. My introduction to the whole spectrum of Asian medicine was therefore one of integration, and I have always been fascinated to see where systems overlap, support and also contradict each other. As human beings we essentially have the same body. There is surprisingly little difference in our basic structure and appearance. But climate and geography have played an important part in shaping the way we view our bodies and the type of medical systems to evolve in different parts of the world. For example, in northern China, where much of Chinese medicine was formalised, it is very cold in the winter and a great emphasis was placed on keeping the body warm and on conserving energy during the winter months. Hence the development of techniques such as moxibustion and the importance of storing and preserving energy. In India the preoccupation would more likely be to keep the body cool, but with an emphasis on maintaining a strong 'digestive fire' to combat the various bugs and parasites which thrive in hot climates. Transporting an indigenous system to another part of the globe must always be done with care and consideration of these factors. And any comparison of the Chinese and Indian systems of either medicine or spiritual practice must always remember the specific roots of each philosophy.

China, lying mostly within the temperate zone, has four distinct seasons, and the observation of nature necessary for the production of food in these conditions led to the development of a world view encompassing ideas of change and transformation based on the cycles of the year. In India the climate has less variation, crops are grown and harvested throughout the year and there is less sense of the seasonal change. The Chinese language is one of association and pattern, the characters evoking a visual more than verbal meaning, it is circular rather than linear, promoting a kind of thinking by poetic association. On the other hand, Sanskrit, the root of all modern Indian languages, is based on sound and vibration and is constructed in a linear way.

Chinese thinking has been traditionally preoccupied with the world and immortality, Indian with enlightenment and the escape from cycles of rebirth. It is the centuries of pre-occupation with something other than the physical realm which still permeates India to this day and makes it a place of pilgrimage and retreat from the material West. Despite its chaos and noise, India remains something 'other', somehow not quite of the world. Both the Chinese and Indian philosophical systems are thousands of years old, the early yogic teachings of India dating from the ancient civilisations of the Indus Valley, and formalised in the Vedas and Upanishads.

The earliest recorded interchanges between China and India took place in the third century BC. At this time the Yoga Sutras of Patanjali were being compiled in India, and the *Yellow Emperor's Inner Classic* was formalised in China. The Indian King Ashoka converted to Buddhism and sent emissaries far and wide, and it is also suggested that the

Emperor Qin, founder of the Han Dynasty, and responsible for much of the unification of China, travelled to the western mountains in search of a plant of immortality rumoured to exist in India. He was unsuccessful, but sent others in what may have been the first sea voyage between China and India. There are other suggestions of an even earlier meeting of these two cultures, but they are pure speculation based on similarities between philosophical and particularly astrological systems. There is no real evidence of influence until the later Han Dynasty in the first and second centuries AD when the Chinese Empire reached out for the first time to trade and explore beyond its boundaries. At this time there was a definite cross-fertilisation of ideas between the two countries, the Silk Road opened China to trade with the West, and there is evidence of a route southwards into India. Buddhist monks from India made the journey to the Chinese Imperial court and by the first century AD scriptures had been translated into Chinese from both Sanskrit and Pali. Sea trade was also flourishing and Chinese ships are known to have reached Sri Lanka, which also converted to Buddhism at this time.

In later centuries Bodhidharma (479–543 AD) travelled from southern India to China by sea. He built a monastery at Shaolin which became famous for its martial arts training. The ancient Indian martial art called Kalarippayattu, which is still practised in the southern Indian state of Kerala, was possibly introduced to China by Bodhidharma and may have had considerable influence on the development of martial arts in the Far East.

Where similarities occur in different cultures there is always an assumption of exchange – but our bodies are essentially the same and it is not altogether surprising that the ancient seer-physicians saw a similar pattern of reality, though often describing it in a different way according to their cultural world view. Despite this later exchange of ideas, particularly in the field of Buddhism, the world views of China and India remained quite distinct, and exchange of ideas within the medical traditions tended to remain within the confines of herbal medicine. Each system was quite complete and although possibly providing thought and inspiration, seemed to do little in changing the fundamental ideas.

THE FIVE ELEMENTS

This difference in perspective can be well illustrated by the two very distinct understandings of what in both systems are called the five elements. There have been many attempts to compare these two systems, but they are at heart totally different in concept. The Chinese theory of the five elements, water, fire, earth, wood and metal, is based on yin and yang and the observation of the changes in nature throughout the four seasons. It is circular, and concerns phases and tendencies of movement and change. Earth is placed in the centre, providing a basis for the change and transformation of the other elements. Related to the cycle of the year and the cycle of the day, wood is the movement of expansion of energy seen at dawn and in spring. It is placed in the east to align with the rising sun. Metal is the movement of contraction, it is the beginning of yin and relates to sunset, the west and the autumn equinox. These two movements of expansion and contraction form the horizontal axis of life on earth, facilitating movement between the two poles of north and south. Fire relates to summer, midday and the south (which is always placed at the top in Chinese representations of space). It has an upward tendency. Water represents winter, midnight and the north. It moves downwards (Plate 8 page 46).

This early Chinese five-element picture is often described as having a horizontal and a vertical axis. The horizontal axis has its centre in the earth, the wood element and the metal element at its extremities. This is often called the earthly axis, as wood and metal are representative of the manifestation of life on earth, the expansion of the wood element constantly controlled by the contraction of the metal. Wood and metal are used to create tools and weapons – they are used in a practical way to enable survival. The vertical axis has water at the base, with its downward cooling movement, fire above with its upward heating movement, earth as a balance in the centre. When applied to the body, the water element controls the lower abdomen and the sexual function; earth the upper abdomen and the digestive function; the fire element the heart and the circulatory function. It is this vertical axis of the five elements that forms the three heaters or burning spaces, which control transformation of substances and the production of energy. The lower heater producing the defensive qi, the middle heater the nutritive qi, the upper heater the ancestral or gathering qi. And it is this vertical axis and the concept of the three heaters which has some characteristics in common with the Indian system.

In the Indian theory the five elements – earth, water, fire, air and space (ether) – represent a linear development from the most material to the most ethereal, and within the body the elements are seen again in a linear pattern with earth controlling the lower parts of the body, ether the uppermost. The Indian system of chakras or energy centres is similarly seen as a progression from the more dense to the more subtle, the chakras as centres of change and interchange of energy of one frequency to another. The earth element controls the area of the base chakra, water the sexual centre, fire the solar plexus, air the heart, space or ether the throat. The brow and crown chakras are above the distinction of the elements, much as the upper dan tian is above the differentiation into yin and yang.

The five elements in Indian thought form a continuum from pure energy to matter, each representing a different state of being. Ether or space is the most subtle, the most rarefied and contains the potential of all the others. It is literally the space through which the other elements are able to come into being. It is all-pervading and motionless. It is related to sound and the sense organ of the ear. Air represents the gaseous state, energy in motion. It is likened to the wind, and manifests itself as subtle energy or prana. Within the physical body it is related to the skin and the sense of touch. Fire – at the centre – is the ability to change from one state to another, the alchemical fire of change and transformation. But it is also light, and the way that form may be seen and differentiated. It is linked with the eyes and the sense of sight. Within the physical body it also controls the digestive fire. Water, the liquid state, is able to change its form, taking the shape of its container, but there is less movement than in the fire or air states. It is said to be 'the physical universe in the process of arranging itself', and is visualised as a vast ocean of still water. Within the body it is the bodily fluids and the sense of taste. Earth is the most dense and solid, it relates to the ground on which we live, and signifies physical existence, weight and cohesion. Energy here is vibrating at a lower frequency. Its subtle sense is smell.

The five elements are represented by geometrical shapes which carry the vibration of their form: earth is a yellow square – the number four represented by the square symbolising matter in most cultures; water is the milky white crescent moon contained within a circle of still water; fire a red inverted triangle; air a blue-grey hexagon; ether a dark circle – the void full of potential. The five elements are illustrated as governing different parts of the body: the earth element the feet to the sacrum; the water element the sacrum to the navel; the fire element the navel to the heart;

the air element the heart to the throat; the ether element the throat to the brow. The Chinese also represent earth as a square, heaven as a circle, and these symbols are seen in all aspects of daily life, including Chinese coinage which is round with a square hole at the centre (Plate 11).

THE THREE DOSHAS

According to Ayurvedic theory, the five elements appear in the human body as vital energy (prana), subtle fire (tejas) and essence (ojas), which share obvious characteristics in common with the three treasures, prana resembling qi, and essence jing. Subtle fire is more akin to the fire of the gate of destiny than to shen (spirit), which is immaterial and related to the power of heaven. Many yogic practices describe the sublimation and transformation of ojas (essence) in a way that resembles the description in the later Daoist alchemical texts of the transformation of sexual essence. It is in these later teachings of Daoist alchemical practice that closer links with the Indian yoga system may be surmised.

Vital energy, subtle fire and essence further manifest themselves within the human body as the three doshas or humours, which are used to classify body type within the practice of Ayurvedic medicine (Plate 12). Prana relates to vata (wind), it is made up of the elements of air and ether and is dry, cold, light, unstable, clear and subtle. Subtle fire relates to pitta which is a combination of fire and water and is hot, intense, light and mobile. Essence relates to kapha, a combination of the earth and water elements, which is oily, cold, heavy, stable, smooth and soft. Differential diagnosis through the doshas is central to Ayurvedic medicine, particularly for the prescription of herbal medicine. But for our purpose here it is the subtle energy system of the Indian body view that is of particular interest.

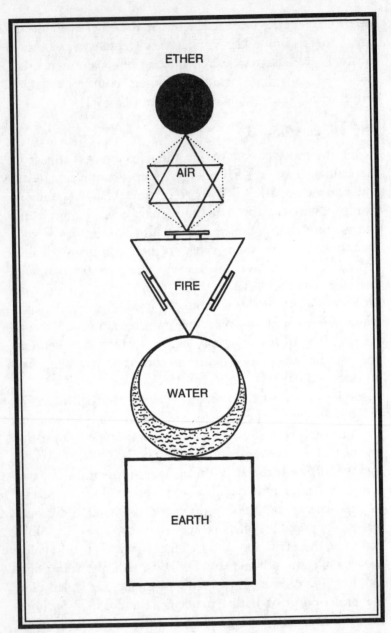

Plate 11

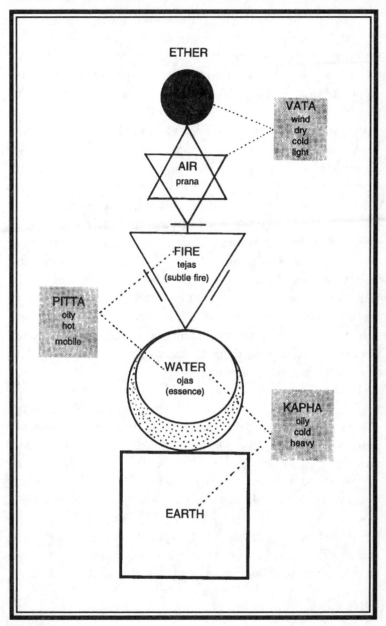

Plate 12

Prana is the breath or lifeforce and appears to be very similar to the Chinese concept of qi. The different types of qi and their relation to the three burning spaces closely resemble the Indian idea of the different types of prana residing in the upper, middle and lower sections of the trunk. In both cases the diaphragm acts as a kind of filtering system for the protection of the heart and lungs; only the most pure and subtle qi or prana can reside in the upper part of the body. We have seen the Chinese classification of qi into the ancestral or zong qi of the upper heater, the nutritive or ying qi of the middle heater and the defensive or wei qi of the lower heater all maintained by the original or yuan qi which originates at the gate of destiny. Similarly Ayurveda describes five types of prana: upana being the finest, which has an upward movement, and is centred in the head; vyana which has a pervasive movement and is centred at the throat; prana which has a forward movement and is centred in the chest; samana which has an equalising movement and is centred in the upper abdomen; apana which has a downward movement and is centred in the lower abdomen.

It is in the movements of these five types of prana that we also see the closest resemblance to the Chinese system of the five elements, which describes each element as a movement: water downward, fire upward, metal contracting, wood expansive, earth equalising. It is interesting to see that similar observations about the energy system of the body may have been made, though the images used to explain these observations may appear contradictory. It is in the movement of qi that the five elements of Chinese medicine have their basis; but it is the varying density and subtlety of energy and matter that is the foundation of the Indian system (Plate 13).

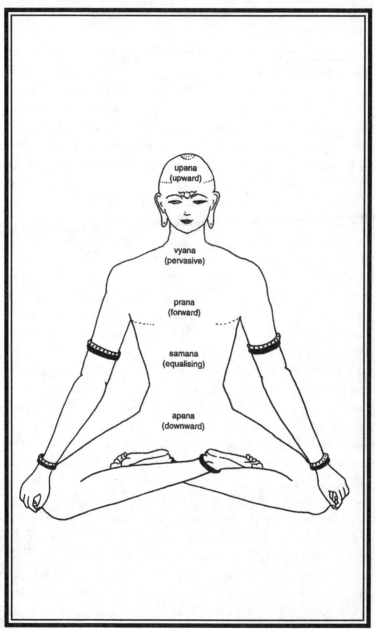

Plate 13

THE SUBTLE ENERGY SYSTEM

In Chinese medicine the qi flows through the acupuncture meridians (jing luo); in the Indian system, prana flows through a system of nadis. The term 'nadi' actually means stream and refers to any kind of circulatory mechanism which can include the blood vessels, the nervous system, etc. The Chinese term meridian is a loose translation of a series of Chinese ideograms which are generally used in couples to gain a more precise meaning. For example 'jing' is translated as meridian, and generally refers to the twelve main energy channels associated to the internal organs. When put together with the term 'luo' to form the jing luo it has the meaning of all the pathways of qi from the twelve main meridians to all the subtle branches and interconnections throughout the body. Jing mai could be translated as all the circulation throughout the acupuncture meridians, the blood vessels, and implies the circulation of blood and qi. Similarly, the gross nadi are the nerves and blood vessels, the pranavaha nadi the channels of prana or vital force, and the equivalent of the acupuncture meridians. The manovaha nadi are said to be channels for the mental force, the pathways of the mind. As qi provides all possible exchange and interchange between heaven and earth, prana is the force which links the physical with the mental, the mental with the spiritual aspects of our being.

The Chinese made an in-depth study of the energy channels and they provide the basis of acupuncture, massage, exercise and even herbal medicine in China. The Indian classics mention the existence of 72,000 nadis, but fourteen are given more full attention. They form an important though sometimes neglected basis for yoga practice. Particularly important for our study are the three main nadis which are closely connected to the spine and the energy plexuses called the chakras. Known as the ida, the pingala and the sushumna, these three subtle energy channels are the focus of meditation practice in much the same way that the two primary yin and yang channels form the basis of Daoist alchemy.

The sushumna nadi is the central canal which corresponds closely to the primary yang channel, the governor vessel or du mai of acupuncture. The prana is said to travel through the sushumna nadi from the base of the spine to the cave of Brahman, the hollow space between the two hemispheres of the brain. Some sources claim that the sushumna begins deep within the abdomen behind the navel, others that it begins in the muladhara or base chakra. This again mirrors the dual expression of the primary yin and yang channels which are said in certain classical texts to begin deep within the abdomen, in others in the perineum. It seems that this knot of energy deep within the abdomen is the source of all life and all energy flow, and in that sense can certainly be seen as the source of these primary energy channels.

The sushumna rises through the spine, penetrating the spinal plexuses or chakras. It enters the brain and divides into two pathways, one anterior, one posterior, closely resembling our diagram of the Tang Dynasty body map. The posterior branch flows through the hind brain and to the top of the head, where it penetrates the crown chakra; the anterior branch through the pituitary and pineal glands to meet up with the posterior branch at the brow centre.

The base chakra is also the source of the ida and pingala, which are said to flow either side of the sushumna. The ida is on the left and corresponds to the moon. Its effect is to cool and calm. The pingala flows on the right and corresponds to the sun. It creates heat and is dynamic in nature. The pingala nadi makes the body more dynamic and vital, the ida gives relaxation with heightened mental awareness. Some ancient texts describe these nadis as flowing on the right and left of the sushumna until they unite in the brow centre; others describe the two nadis as intersecting at each of the energy centres. However, there is agreement that the ida ends in the left nostril, the pingala in the right (Plate 14).

The yoga practice of alternate nostril breathing, which we will discuss in more detail later, aims to balance the ida and pingala. Breathing through the left nostril, known sometimes as moon breathing, is calming and cooling, mentally stimulating and purifying. Breathing through the right nostril, referred to as solar breathing, increases stamina, vitality and cleanses like fire. The safest way to activate and balance these two channels is to practise alternate nostril breathing in which alternate nostrils are closed by the fingers to assure that each is used with equal effect. Modern scientific research has suggested a connection between the ida and pingala and the sympathetic and parasympathetic nerves of the autonomic nervous system. There have also been suggested correspondences with the functions of the left and right hemispheres of the brain.

A further seven nadis are mentioned in some texts as belonging to the upper and lower orifices, and pathways are described from the toes to the eyes, the toes to the ears, the anus to the mouth, the throat to the genitals, the throat to the anus. There are striking similarities between the descriptions of these ten nadis and the ancient descriptions of the eight extraordinary meridians which form the basic structure of the subtle energy system in Chinese medicine and the energetic pattern on which the physical body is based.

The practice known as purification of the sushumna is traditionally the prerequisite of all meditational practice, much in the same way as the circulation of light is used in Daoist yoga. The aim of yoga practice is to allow the

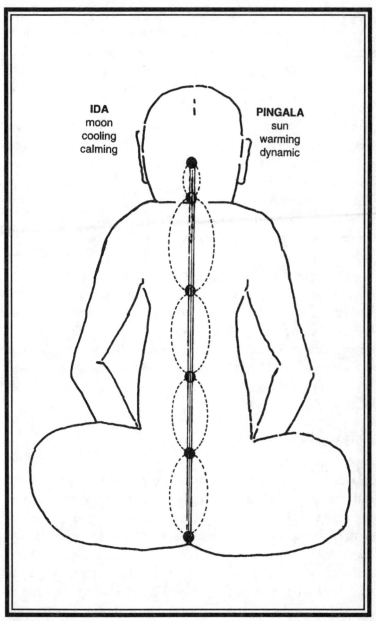

Plate 14

uninterrupted flow of prana through the subtle energy channels within the spinal cord – to unite the lower centres of physical energy with pure consciousness. Much of physical yoga, or hatha yoga practice, aims to align the spinal vertebrae and promote the flow of prana within the subtle energy channels in preparation for pranayama (breath control) and dhyana (concentration). Sushumna cleansing performs a similar function on the energetic or subtle level, using the breath and the imagination to clear and strengthen the channel. If the sushumna is clear of obstructions, pure energy is activated in the base chakra. It rises through the subtle energy channels to the crown chakra. In turn pure consciousness is able to fully penetrate the physical body.

The dormant energy that resides at the base of the spine is called kundalini. It is depicted as a sleeping serpent coiled within the base chakra. It is Shakti, pure energy, as opposed to Shiva, pure consciousness, and it is the meeting of Shiva and Shakti, energy and consciousness, that is the aim of all yoga practice. Kundalini Shakti is the power of the goddess, the synthesiser of forces while the soul is within a physical body. The union of these male and female forces is the basis of tantrism.

THE THREE OBSTRUCTIONS

The Indian rishis have identified three knots or granthi which tend to create obstructions to this process of unification. These knots are located in the lower abdomen, at the heart and between the eyebrows, each having its root within the spinal cord. They resemble the locations of the three dan tian in Chinese alchemy, and could possibly be linked to the gates along the spinal column which we saw in the inner landscape of the body (Plate 15). The first knot is called the Brahma Granthi, the knot of Brahma. Brahma is the creator and is known as the god of the world of name

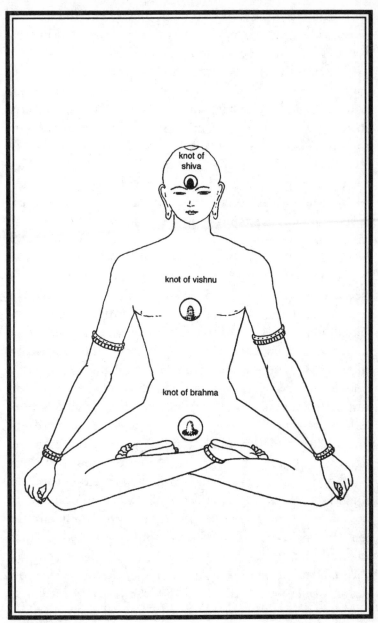

Plate 15

and form. It is related to the physical body and the material world. The world of name and form includes everything that we can grasp with the five senses; attachment to the world of name and form creates desires and ambitions. Untying this knot is said to free us from the bonds of attachment to the material world. Whether our attachments are to material possessions, to sex, to security, this is the knot that we must untie to become free of these limitations.

The second knot is the knot of Vishnu, which is located at the heart chakra. This knot concerns emotional attachment. Vishnu is the god of preservation. He keeps the world as it is, preserving family loyalties and spiritual traditions which tend to be fed by the energy of the heart chakra, by devotion, faith and love. Emotional attachment includes attachment to compassion, attachment to helping others, as well as more negative emotional attachments. It is also the desire to keep things as they are. The knot of Vishnu must be untied when this kind of attachment becomes a bond, when it prevents personal evolution. It must be untied by knowledge, wisdom and true discrimination. This is a knowledge or breadth of vision which is able to see the real purpose of the universe, the divine plan beyond all traditions and institutions. It also concerns detachment from deep-seated patterns within the individual, possibly the inherited patterns within the genetic code. When the knot of Vishnu is untied the individual is able to move forward beyond the limitations created by emotional ties and commitments to traditions. In order to go beyond the ties to family and the genetic code the practice of asceticism arose in India, which involved giving up family and status in the search for spiritual truth. Traditionally, the family of the sannyasa, as the ascetic would be called, would perform funeral rites which would enable the individual to free himself from the deep ties of family and begin to loosen the ties of the genetic code. It is related to the astral body and the world of emotions.

The final knot is at the brow centre, the area of the third eye, it is called the knot of Rudra, or the knot of Shiva. It is at the brow centre that the two nadis, the ida and pingala, meet. It is seen to be beyond duality, beyond the distinctions of the five elements, beyond the confines of time and space. It is related to the causal body and the world of thought, ideas and visions. In yoga theory the knot that must be untied is the knot of attachment to intuitive vision and psychic powers. At each level it is the very mechanism of growth and development that must then be left behind in order to move on.

These three knots correspond to the second, fourth, and sixth chakras, which have their roots within the spinal cord and their trigger points on the front of the body.

THE CHAKRAS

The chakras are the psychic centres of energy exchange and interchange. They are the crossing point of the nadis, connected to the main nerve plexuses and ductless glands within the physical body. There are seven main chakras which have their roots along the spinal cord from the coccyx to the top of the head. Their flowers or trigger points are located on the front midline of the body. For health it is important that these energy centres are functioning in a balanced way, without one centre being over-used, another under-used. For spiritual development it is necessary for the centres to be open to allow the unhampered flow of energy from the base of the spine to the crown of the head and also to allow the exchange and interchange of energy between the more physical and more subtle dimensions. These 'wheels of light' act as converters of energy from one dimension to another, their functions embrace physical, emotional, mental and spiritual aspects of the self. In understanding their interdimensional nature, we can begin to understand the true mechanisms of healing.

We all have blocks in certain areas, and an understanding of the chakras can help us to identify those blocks and work with them consciously. Recent work in the West by healers and psychics has clarified the particular psychological states which resonate with the mental and emotional energies of each chakra. This work has been very valuable in aiding our understanding of how emotional and mental states affect the physical body and verifies many of the ancient Indian teachings. This kind of awareness, brought together with physical exercise, breath control and concentration of the mind, will prove to be the most valuable tool in the future of health care. To affect the mind we can use the body. To affect the body we can use the mind. The chakras are the key to the mind/body connection, they integrate all levels of our being. Within each chakra there are physical, emotional and mental aspects, and transformation within the chakra takes place on all these levels (Plate 16).

Some of the discrepancies that occur between descriptions of the chakras by different teachers may be due to the fact that the chakras exist on these different levels. Traditional Indian teaching on the chakras tells us that consciousness is able to exist in five bodies or sheaths: the physical body (the sheath of matter, the annamaya kosha), the vital or energy body (the sheath of prana, the pranamaya kosha); the mental body (the sheath of mind, the manomaya kosha); the sheath of knowledge (the vijnamaya kosha); the sheath of bliss (the anandamaya kosha). These various energy bodies co-exist and energy is constantly transformed between one body and another. An imbalance within the mental body will eventually become an imbalance within the physical body, and unless the mental cause is affected, there will be no

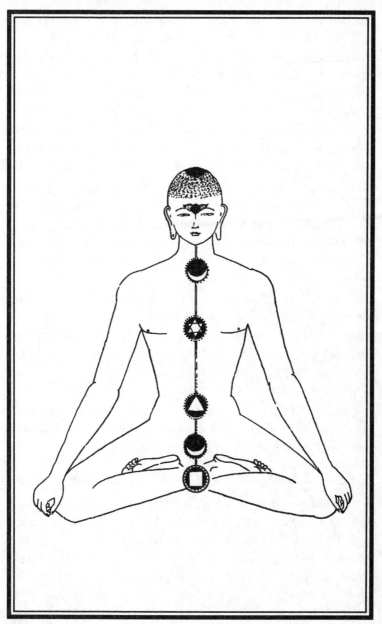

Plate 16

permanent cure. The physical symptoms may be addressed, but the distortion in the mental body will eventually recreate the problem. The chakras exist in all these dimensions, and have been seen by psychics in different forms and colours, depending on their level of vision. Each chakra resonates more closely with a specific plane of consciousness, but there are overlaps between these various levels, following a basic movement from the most dense and physical, upwards and outwards to the most subtle.

In tantric yoga each chakra has a specific diagram (yantra) which is a representation of its vibration. In the same way that sand on a sheet of metal will form different shapes according to the resonance of a particular note, so within the science of yoga, sound and geometric form (mantra and yantra) are used to express the energetic resonance of each chakra. These diagrams are often visualised during meditation to aid attunement with the chakra. Some yantras are purely geometric, others are in the form of flowers and contain representations of the gods and goddesses of Indian mythology which symbolise consciousness in its various manifestations.

Descriptions of the chakras are many, varied and often highly complex. Here we will attempt to keep to the classical Indian descriptions, though simplifying details.

The Base Chakra – Muladhara – the Foundation

Located at the base of the spine, the base or root chakra is our root in the physical body. In Sanskrit it is called muladhara or foundation. Unlike the other centres it is not differentiated into root and flower, but is located at a single point within the perineum between the anus and the genitals. It relates to the pelvic nerve plexus. Its organ of function is the anus, its associated sense is smell, its sense organ the nose. It controls the process of giving birth, and ejaculation during the male orgasm. It is the primitive push for birth and life.

This energy centre is the basis of life from birth until the age of seven. It helps the individual to develop the necessary skills for survival in the physical world, regulating the patterns of eating and drinking, sleeping and waking. It is the centre of the primitive self, the centre of our animal consciousness, controlling the instinctual animal responses for survival. It controls our will to live and our sense of security in the world. If the adult is still functioning from a base chakra level, there may be violent behaviour originating in deep insecurity, often from trauma during the first seven years of life. It is the centre of illusion, anger, greed — but it is also the foundation of all growth and evolution. It is from here that our desire for growth emerges. A refusal to acknowledge first chakra issues will provide a spirituality based on illusion, an experience without roots. A functional first chakra will provide a reliable basis in reality, stable physical energy and the will to live in the physical world rather than to escape into fantasy.

The base chakra is related to the earth element, and is symbolised by a chrome yellow square with four red petals. It represents the four directions, the four dimensions. Within the square is the inverted triangle representing the kundalini force, and from the triangle the three energy channels, the ida, pingala and shushumna ascend (Plate 17).

The animal or vehicle related to the base chakra is the elephant, its strength and stability providing a firm foundation. In its slow and majestic way the elephant constantly searches for food — for the body, mind and spirit. The elephant in the base centre has seven trunks, which represent the seven chakras. They symbolise the seven senses which need to be controlled — defecation, sex, smell, taste, sight, touch, sound; the seven work organs — the anus, genitals, nose, tongue, eyes,

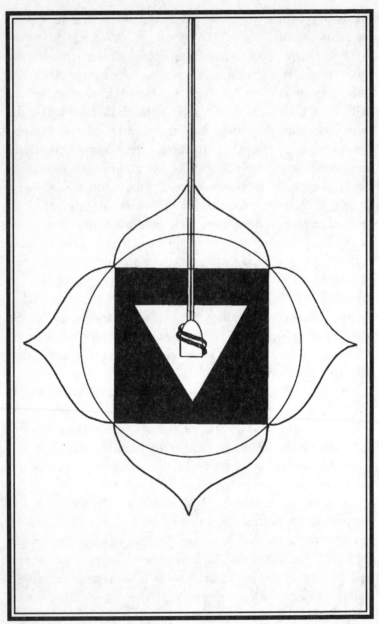

Plate 17 – The Base Chakra

skin, ears; the seven constituents of the human body – earth, fluids, blood, tissues, fat, bone, bone marrow; and the seven types of desire – for security, procreation, longevity, sharing, knowledge, self-realisation and union. The seven trunks are often depicted in the seven colours of the rainbow, they are associated with each of the seven chakras, the seven musical notes and the seven major planets.

The deity of the muladhara chakra is Ganesha, the elephant-headed god. Classically he is the remover of obstacles, the protector of all undertakings and new beginnings. Mythologically Ganesha is the son of Shiva. He carries the swastika, symbol of the union of the four directions.

The Shakti or goddess of the first chakra has four arms. In one hand she holds a trident which combines the forces of creation, destruction and preservation, the characteristics of Brahma, Shiva and Vishnu. In the second she holds a skull, which represents triumph over the fear of death, the strongest psychological block of the first chakra. In her other two hands she holds a sword to remove ignorance and a shield for protection.

The Second Chakra – Swadhisthana – the Centre of the Self

Located within the lower abdomen, with its root at the base of the spine, this centre is closely related to sexual function. In Sanskrit it is called swadhisthana or the dwelling place of the self. Its organ of function is the genitals, its associated sense is taste, its sense organ the tongue. It controls the process of individuation and sexual development.

This energy centre is the basis of life from age seven to fourteen. Once we are able to look after our primitive survival needs, we begin to develop associations with others. The child creates relationships with family and friends.

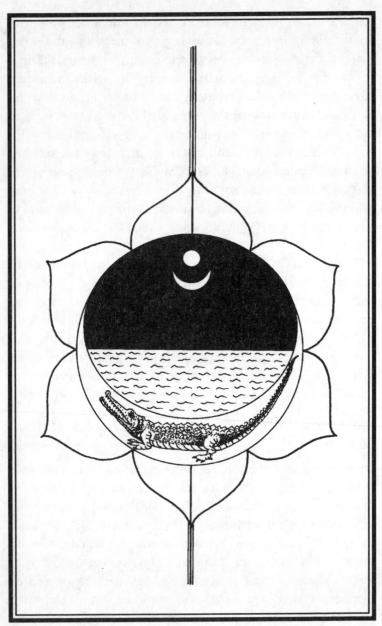

Plate 18 – The Second Chakra

Feeling more secure, there is room for creativity and imagination, there is the beginning of awareness of the physical body and an awakening of sensuality. The second chakra is the centre for the development of the individual personality, and the attempt to create balance between the inner and outer worlds.

Governed by the moon, with its constantly changing cycles and phases, the adult based in the second chakra may be affected by emotional instability. There may be restlessness and confusion, desires and sexual fantasies. Envy and jealousy may arise from the need to possess. Opening the second chakra brings freedom from desires and ambitions. It brings the ability to move freely in the physical world without attachment. A balanced second chakra will give the ability to give and take in personal relationships, to enjoy a sexual relationship in which there is a beneficial exchange of energies between partners.

The second chakra is related to the water element, and is symbolised by a pale blue crescent moon within a circle of milky white. Its flower has six deep red petals, said to be the colour of mercuric oxide – the alchemist's stone. The animal related to the swadhisthana chakra is the crocodile. It is symbolic of the unconscious, of sexual desire and sensuality. It loves to float on the water, and mythologically is associated with trickery and fantasy. Traditionally crocodile fat was used by Indian men to enhance their sexual performance (Plate 18).

The deity represented within the second chakra is Vishnu, the god of preservation. Through procreation he ensures the continuation of the species. He is able to take on different physical forms at will and is the hero in the cosmic drama, whether as Rama the god-king of the Ramayana or Krishna, adviser to Arjuna in the *Mahabharata* and Arjuna's charioteer in the battle which formed the backdrop to the *Bhagavad*

Gita. He embodies the principles of truth. Vishnu's four hands hold the wheel or chakra, spinning on his index finger, which represents time, the cosmic rhythm. In many Indian stories Krishna will suddenly hurl his wheel of light to decapitate an enemy of the truth. Essentially his task is to preserve the cosmic rhythm – anything working against the cosmic rhythm cannot survive. He also holds a metal club, to show his authority over the earth, a conch shell for sounding the cosmic sound and a lotus. The lotus flower is so revered in Indian mythology as it has its roots deep in the mud at the bottom of the pool, but flowers in perfection. It symbolises the purification process.

The Shakti or goddess of the second chakra has two heads, which represent the split between the inner and outer worlds. She is the goddess of desires and fantasies and she gives the first inspiration for music and art. She is also said to be the goddess of the vegetable kingdom, and traditionally a vegetarian diet is recommended while working on this centre.

The Third Chakra – the Solar Plexus, the Centre of Individual Power

The flower of the third chakra is located at the navel. It is related to the solar plexus and has its root on the spine at the level of the waist. Its Sanskrit name is manipura, city of jewels. Its areas of function are the feet and legs, its sense is sight, its sense organ the eyes. This centre aids the digestion and absorption of food and the digestion and absorption of ideas. It governs vision.

The manipura chakra begins to operate from the age of fourteen through to twenty-one. It allows the developing being to function and develop an ego identity in the world. The individual operating from the third chakra will be preoccupied with goals of personal achievement, fame and recognition, possibly at the expense of others. The lesson of the third chakra is to remain true to one's own nature. By remaining true to one's own nature relationships with others will become stable. If the third chakra is functioning well there will be a sense of being in one's proper place in the universe.

The manipura chakra is governed by the fire element. Its yantra is a red inverted triangle within a white circle; it has ten dark blue petals. It is ruled by the sun and its associated animal is the ram – the vehicle of Agni, the sun god. The ram charges into things head first, often with little concern for the consequences (Plate 19).

The deity is old Shiva, representing the power of destruction. This is the self-obsessed ascetic, searching for immortality, longevity and personal power. The Shakti or goddess within the manipura chakra has three heads, symbolising that her vision encompasses the three planes of existence. She holds a thunderbolt, an arrow and the celestial fire. Her fourth hand forms the mudra (hand gesture) of fearlessness. Armed with the arrow from the god Kama, she is able to transform the ego energy of the third chakra upwards towards the heart. Her teaching at the level of the third chakra is selfless service.

The Fourth Chakra – the Heart Centre

The heart centre is located at the centre of the chest, its root is at the same level on the spine between the shoulder blades. In Sanskrit it is anahata, inner or cosmic sound. Its mode of operation is through the hands, it governs the sense of touch and the skin. Its time of development is between twenty-one and twenty-eight; it occupies the central position amongst the chakras and its aim is to balance the three upper and three lower centres.

The element of the anahata chakra is air, representing the

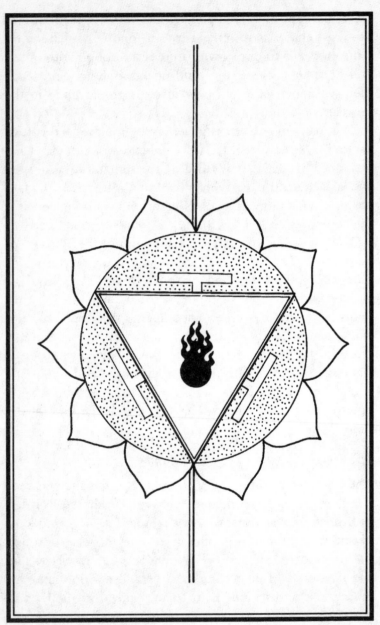

Plate 19 – The Third Chakra

breath of life. Its yantra is the six-pointed star, symbol of the meeting of Shiva and Shakti; the inverted triangle of kundalini Shakti uniting with the upward pointing triangle of Shiva. The six-pointed star represents balance and unity. Here we see Shiva again, but in his youthful aspect. Here he represents detachment from the desires of the physical world. He lives in perpetual happiness, wearing a tiger skin to show the domination of his mind, snakes around his body to symbolise the control of his passions. The old ego-based nature of the third chakra is gone as the male and female principles are brought into balance in the fourth chakra. There is also balance between the internal and external worlds (Plate 20).

The Shakti or goddess of the heart centre has four heads and four hands. She represents balance and harmony. Her four heads symbolise the balance of the physical self, the emotional self, the rational self and the sensual self. In her four hands she holds the trident, the skull, the sword and the shield. Goddess of the air element, she is all-pervading and provides vital energy for the whole body. She inspires devotion and brings creative and visionary expression through music, art and poetry. The creativity of the fourth chakra resonates with the heart and is able to inspire cosmic consciousness. The goddess of the heart chakra inspires bhakti (devotion) – the emotional state of humility when faced with the immensity of cosmic consciousness.

The animal of the heart chakra is the deer. If the heart chakra is unstable, the qualities of the deer may be apparent; there is nervousness and restlessness, coupled with awareness and sensitivity. The deer is capable of deep love, joy and compassion.

The Fifth Chakra – the Throat Centre

The flower of the fifth chakra is located at the base of the

Plate 20 – The Fourth Chakra

throat, its root is at the base of the neck, where the cervical and thoracic vertebrae meet. It is connected with the carotid plexus and the thyroid gland. Its organ of operation is the mouth, its sense is hearing and its sense organ the ears. Its symbol is the silver crescent moon, representing pure cosmic sound and the awakening of psychic powers. In Sanskrit it is vishuddha, to purify. The vishuddha chakra is the chakra of purification and represents purity of thought and speech. Its element is ether, the void from which the other elements are formed and to which they return. It is beyond shape and form (Plate 21).

In the throat centre Shiva is depicted as a deity with five heads and four hands. The five heads symbolise the five senses, as well as the five elements in their purified forms. One hand holds a drum which continually reverberates the cosmic sound, another holds a mala or string of beads for recitation of mantras and the third holds the trident of consciousness. His fourth hand is raised in the gesture to bestow fearlessness. He represents the true guru, the continual awareness of the divine within the individual.

The nectar of purification flows into the throat from the sixth chakra. Mythologically, Shiva is able to swallow any poison and transmute it within his body.

The Shakti of the fifth chakra brings purity. She embodies knowledge, and the correct use of knowledge. Memory, intuition and also dreams are related to the Shakti of the fifth chakra. With her staff she controls the animal of the fifth chakra, the elephant who symbolises intellect and carries all the knowledge of the earth, including the knowledge of herbs and plants. Unlike the elephant of the first chakra, the elephant of the fifth chakra has just one trunk, to symbolise pure sound. All the diverse attributes of the first chakra are combined in the fifth.

The throat chakra governs life between the ages of

Plate 21 – The Fifth Chakra

twenty-eight to thirty-five. It inspires the seeking of true knowledge. Negative aspects of the throat chakra may be in using knowledge unwisely.

The Sixth Chakra – the Brow Centre

The sixth chakra is located between the eyebrows, at the point where the three nadis, the ida (the lunar channel), pingala (the solar channel) and shushumna (the central current), merge to form the third of the knots which must be untied before the kundalini Shakti is able to rise to the top of the head. It is connected with the pineal gland and its root is at the base of the skull. The Sanskrit name is ajna (to know and to command). Its form is a white circle with two luminous petals. Within the circle is the form of Shiva-Shakti, half-male half-female, lifeforce and divine consciousness united in a single being. The male hand holds the trident of Shiva, the female hand a lotus (Plate 22).

The ajna chakra is beyond duality, beyond space and time. In the heart centre the male and female elements were seen to be in balance, here they are united. It is no longer a matter of balancing opposites – here opposites cease to exist. The ajna chakra is said to be above karma. There can therefore be no negative aspect of the sixth centre, it represents the inner conscience, the inner teacher, the inner wisdom. The ajna chakra is beyond the five elements and is said to contain the seed of all the five elements in their most rarefied form. It is the seat of consciousness in its fourfold nature – mind, intellect, identification and being. The sound of the ajna chakra is *aum*, the cosmic sound.

Above the ajna is a smaller centre called the soma or bindu. This is the moon chakra which produces the divine nectar which drips down into the throat. It is here that the kundalini Shakti meets with the transformed male essence, symbolised by Shiva as the lord of desire. Kundalini is no longer the

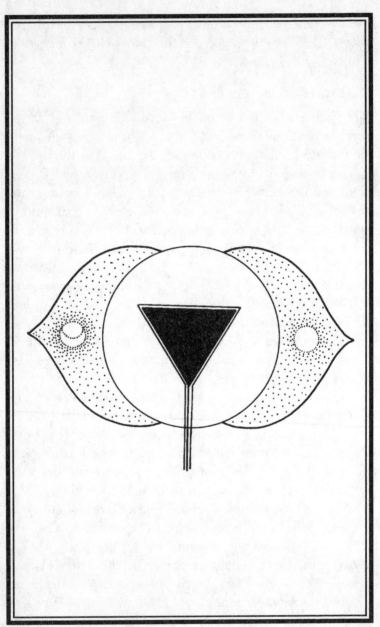

Plate 22 – The Sixth Chakra

dangerous serpent power of the lower chakras, but is at peace, resting in the arms of her beloved. This is one of the many smaller centres sometimes said to exist within the seventh chakra.

The Seventh Centre – the Thousand-Petalled Lotus

The seventh chakra is located at the top of the head. Its name in Sanskrit is the thousand-petalled, and it is also called shunya, the great void. It is the centre of nothingness, of liberation. The mind is still. There is no knowledge, no knower, nothing to be known. The individual is dissolved into oneness. In the sixth chakra there was a unification of all the individual aspects, here there is unification of the individual with the divine. The awakened crown chakra is the sign of the saint, often depicted as a halo of light.

It is from the crown centre that the soul is said to leave the body, and although it is possible for the soul to leave and enter from any of the energy centres, it is the crown centre which allows the soul access to the higher realms. And it is this centre by which the yogi hopes to depart from the physical body at death.

Many spiritual traditions have taught that the aim of practice is the attainment of liberation from the physical. The practice of yoga by ascetics in India has often focused on the release from the physical body and an escape from the cycle of birth and death. But true yoga practice concerns the trans-formation of the physical body to accommodate a higher level of pure consciousness. It concerns the transformation of the body and of life on earth, rather than an abdication from the physical reality and concentration on the afterlife. During this century the teachings of Sri Aurobindo have acted as a focus for a yoga not of transcendence but of transformation. This is a yoga which attempts to transform the physical body. To create a physical body which is capable of receiving higher levels of energy from the cosmos. The evolution of species involves an increasing ability to absorb and transform – to transform the resistance of matter to an increasingly malleable state.

SCIENTIFIC VERIFICATION AND PSYCHIC PHENOMENA

Dr Motoyama's scientific research into the subtle energy system at his Institute for Human Science led him to develop two diagnostic tools; the AMI (Apparatus for measuring the function of the Meridians and their corresponding Internal organs), which measures the energy of the acupuncture meridians, and the so-called 'chakra machine', which is located within a small energy-shielded room resembling a Faraday cage and which measures changes in the electrical field of the body during concentration on the individual chakras. With the information gathered by these two instruments, Dr Motoyama began to make connections between the chakras and the meridians of acupuncture. He noted particular energetic imbalances within the meridian system which suggested a corresponding imbalance within the chakra system. As Shinto priest and psychic, Dr Motoyama was able to discern these patterns extra-sensorially; as a scientist his aim was to prove that these energies did in fact exist, and to provide reliable objective information which could be used to help the individual's progress.

During my stay in Tokyo these diagnostic instruments were in their preliminary stages of development, and many tests were being carried out to ascertain various norms and devi-ations from the norm amongst a varied group of volunteers. As a meditation student and voluntary worker at the Institute, I was tested with the AMI machine on a regular basis. Acupuncture treatment would be based on the AMI diagnosis and meditation practice would often be regulated according to the energy patterns detected by the tests. A state of general instability within the whole meridian system would often be regulated by the practice of the circulation of light; an excess of energy in one or two meridians, and a lack of energy in others, by the practice of specific yoga asanas and concentration to a particular chakra or energy centre.

In Japan and internationally, Dr Motoyama's reputation as a parapsychologist was growing, as was his ability to differentiate schizophrenia from what in Japan would traditionally be seen as spiritual instability or even spirit possession. His reputation for successfully treating some of these cases was also beginning to draw attention to his work. He tested many individuals with unusual abilities with his two diagnostic devices, and the growing data bank began to provide interesting and consistent results. Pooling his understanding of the Chinese system of acupuncture meridians and the Indian chakras with his own personal experiences and clairvoyant abilities, he grouped his subjects into types according to their energetic patterns.

The Second Chakra Type

His findings showed that a particular pattern of instability in the kidney and bladder meridians, along with certain psychic abilities, suggested that the swadhisthana or second chakra was active. This often seemed to be the case with psychics with inborn abilities which were often spontaneous and not under their control. We have seen that the swadhisthana is linked with the unconscious (symbolically represented by the crocodile) and many cases of 'madness' were diagnosed as an inborn psychic ability which had been suppressed or remained uncontrolled.

Activity of the second chakra is said to stir up memories from the unconscious and in the Shinto, Buddhist and Hindu traditions these memories would be described as karmic residues of personal, ancestral and also collective origins. In certain cases of schizophrenia, rather than embark on drug therapy, a spiritual consultation in the Shinto shrine with either Dr Motoyama or his mother would aim to locate the source of the problematic karma, and offerings and prayers would be made to the offending spirits. The individual would undergo a hundred days of prayers, usually chanting the Heart Sutra many times a day. Dr Motoyama would also suggest the circulation of light as the most suitable practice to balance energy within the meridian system, and once some balance had been obtained, concentration on the ajna chakra, the brow centre, the centre above karma, to compensate for the overactivity within the swadhisthana.

The swadhistana is a common area of instability in early spiritual practice, and while working with imbalances in this centre a vegetarian diet would be recommended. A vegetarian diet helps to calm animal impulses and refine the energy. It is also less taxing on the digestive fire, which can then be used more efficiently to transform psychic energies. Because sexual energy may increase with activation of the second chakra, traditionally celibacy would be suggested. The sexual essence (jing, ojas) would be retained within the body and refined rather than depleted by excess sexual activity.

The Hindu tradition teaches that the second chakra stores sexual karma. Attachments of a sexual nature from previous incarnations will tend to manifest themselves in this area, possibly as illness. Also, during prolonged periods of concentration to the second chakra, sexual karma may be activated. This is another reason for the traditional practice of celibacy. In extreme cases severe imbalance in the swadhisthana chakra may provoke violent behaviour, especially violent sexual behaviour, and even individuals who may be normally quite balanced can experience instability if this centre becomes activated.

When I first began studying with Dr Motoyama he was

114

testing a number of subjects who had experienced a psychokinetic phenomenon such as spoon-bending, key-bending and objects moving from one location to another. During one controlled experiment at the Institute a paper weight actually teleported from one room to another. This kind of phenomenon often seems to be quite pointless and occurs spontaneously without conscious control; the individual involved may appear innocent and naive, but is actually 'tricky', the quality related in Hindu tradition with the crocodile of the second chakra. This trickiness seems to imply emotional instability and the emergence of material from the unconscious. To shed 'crocodile tears' is also a traditional Indian saying suggesting inappropriate displays of emotion. Poltergeist phenomena have a similar energy, and are often detected around adolescents unable to control emerging sexuality.

Two of the subjects of these tests had many years of martial arts experience with focus on the development of the hara. In one case tests with the chakra machine showed that energy was emitted in the form of light during concentration on the swadhisthana chakra. If this kind of ability is controlled by spiritual practice, and accompanied by humility, the energy can be channelled into healing and other beneficial work. Traditionally, this kind of power may be associated with a past life in which the individual achieved a considerable amount of personal power, but then abused that power in some way.

The Tibetan tradition suggests that spiritual awakening begins with the third chakra, and they do not mention the first two chakras in their practice. There is a widespread belief, found also within many Western esoteric schools, that if the upper chakras are activated, their beneficial influence will descend to the lower centres, and that working specifically on the lower centres is very dangerous. The

Tantric traditional as taught by Satyananda Saraswati suggests that any work on the two lower centres be preceded by concentration on the eyebrow centre to create the necessary balance. Circulation of the light to balance the meridian system, concentration on the brow centre (the centre above karma) to activate the higher spiritual self, followed by breathing exercises to the lower abdomen would be the method prescribed by Dr Motoyama for imbalances within the second chakra.

Instabilities in the Third Chakra

A pattern of instability within the spleen and stomach, and occasionally liver and gall bladder meridians, detected by the AMI would be linked with instability in the manipura or third chakra. Traditionally this chakra is associated with receiving psychic energy, with extra-sensory perception and telepathic ability. In the acupuncture tradition, the spleen controls the reception of ideas, and a weakened or erratic spleen energy may result in the inability to discern what are one's own thoughts and the thoughts of others. There may be a possibility of possession or adverse effects from another's energy, due to a lack of discernment and protection in this area. In Chinese medicine the liver is associated with the hun (soul), and with vision and imagination. It is the hun that is said to leave the body during astral projection.

Individuals with this kind of pattern would often have the ability to receive information from others in the form of telepathy. They also could have a tendency to be over-affected by the energies of other individuals – alive or dead. Possession is a commonplace assumption in Japan. Ghost stories are a popular form of entertainment and usually involve the possession of an individual by a wandering soul or unhappy ghost. Often there is a personal or ancestral link between the individual and the deceased involving some wrong doing. The wrong must be acknowledged, if possible put right, and prayers made for the lost soul to send it on its way to the next world.

I remember the old tale of a young monk who was haunted by a particularly persistent ghost, drowned during the bloody Heike wars of eleventh-century Japan. The tortured soul was unable to accept its death, unable to accept defeat in battle, unable to forgive its enemies. Each night the monk was painted head to toe with protective sutras. He chanted from dusk until dawn for the release of the soul from its eternal suffering. Each time the individual disembodied soul released its anger and hatred, another came to take its place, until finally the whole defeated Heike army rose from the sea.

An early death in battle may prevent the soul from leaving the physical plane; anger, pain, and the need for revenge often hold the soul trapped at the moment of death, unable to move. An important part of Dr Motoyama's work as a Shinto priest involved the cleansing of old battle sites. His meditation retreat to the south of Tokyo was built on such a site, and prayers were made constantly for the release of the suffering souls.

It was during a retreat at this particular centre that I first became aware of what I later understood to be possession. I began to experience pain and sensitivity in the middle of my back, in the area of the tenth and eleventh thoracic vertebrae, which I originally attributed to an injury in the aikido dojo. In acupuncture terms this area corresponds with the spleen meridian, and in the Indian system with the manipura chakra. AMI readings consistently showed an imbalance in the spleen energy – often a left/right instability, occasionally an excess of energy and often an insufficiency. During a weekend meditation retreat I began to sense the presence of ghosts and beings from other dimensions, an experience that would often be accompanied by nausea and sometimes a tugging sensation around the navel.

I had come to Japan quite sceptical of spiritual other worldliness. I had originally chosen Zen as a path I could follow because it seemed very down to earth and I could explain most of its teachings in modern psychological terminology. The Zen breathing classes I attended when I first arrived were full of middle-aged women and old men in strange underwear. I liked the normality with which this practice was treated in Japan. When I first encountered Dr Motoyama I was drawn to his scientific approach and his attempt to explain the results of spiritual practice in a rational and acceptable way. I suppose I had always considered myself to have a reasonable grip on reality, but from the time that I arrived in Japan this feeling of reality and normality was gradually eroded.

Gradually over the following months I became aware of a dark shadowy presence during meditations at my home, and during my sleep I would suddenly awake in terror unable to move. In this state of immobility I realised that I could see the room with my eyes closed, and that I could also see what was behind me. At the beginning it was difficult to differentiate these experiences from a dream state, but gradually the signs became familiar, and as my fear became more under control I began to explore my surroundings.

After a particularly vivid encounter, when I had total recollection of leaving the body through the exact area of sensitivity on my back, I decided to talk to Dr Motoyama about my experience. 'Your experiences are from the manipura chakra,' he said, in a matter of fact way. 'From the manipura it is easy to access the lower astral dimensions which are full of hungry ghosts. You must learn to raise your energy to one of the higher centres and your experience will be less frightening.'

According to the Hindu tradition, the manipura chakra is the level of the self, and the fear of the manipura may be described as the fear of the loss of the self. My unwillingness to accept many of the experiences I had when I first arrived in Japan were somehow symbolic of my fear of the loss of my self, of my identity. In the classical descriptions of the chakras it is mentioned that an awakened manipura chakra brings a feeling of being at peace within the world, of finding one's true nature. This seems to be possible by transcending the feeling of ego separateness of the manipura, and offering the self to the divine. The goddess of the manipura chakra symbolises selfless service.

The spleen, as the organ in Chinese medicine closely associated by Dr Motoyama with the manipura chakra, is governed by the earth element. It is located between the water of the kidneys and the fire of the heart and must constantly keep these two elements in balance. The spiritual aspect of the spleen is called the yi, usually translated as 'purpose'. The Chinese character for 'yi' is made with a musical note and the heart, and for the spleen centre to function well, the purpose must be in resonance with the heart. Its wisdom is achieved by remaining grounded and offering all thoughts and perceptions to the heart. If one remains grounded and yet open to the influence of heaven, there is no way the hungry ghosts can enter. A purpose aligned with divine will, or our higher nature, is our protection.

Once these encounters were explained and I was given instructions to pray for the souls of those who came to me, my fear began to decrease. After a few months of consistent practice, the AMI readings began to show a more stable pattern, and the hauntings gradually subsided. I noticed that on an emotional level I was able to take more responsibility for my own actions, I felt less vulnerable, less willing to be at the mercy of external circumstances. While diving into a swimming pool around this time, my back twisted in an unusual way and I feared that I had damaged the vertebrae.

But it turned out that the action had allowed the misplaced tenth and eleventh vertebrae to realign, and I experienced no more pain and sensitivity.

This sequence of events occurring on the physical, emotional and psychic levels created a graphic illustration of the interconnectedness of mind, body and spirit. Though difficult to explain with words, I somehow understood the connections within my body.

Activity in the Heart Centre

So instability within the lower centres and within the kidney and bladder meridian function tends to show an inborn but often unconscious psychic ability; a similar instability in the third chakra and within the spleen and stomach meridians suggests a tendency to extra-sensory perception. The third category is the instability of the heart chakra and the heart and heart protector (pericardium) meridians. Dr Motoyama found that this group often had the ability to send energy, whereas the former group tended to be energy- or information-receivers. Of the many people tested with the AMI and the chakra machine, amongst those who showed patterns of instability, or unusually high levels of energy within the heart meridians, were many healers and advanced practitioners of martial arts. During the development of the diagnostic machines, Dr Motoyama tested many healers and yoga practitioners, including some of the psychic surgeons from the Philippines, and several yogis from India who were able to use their breath to control the involuntary processes of the autonomic nervous system, and even the heart rate.

During the latter part of my stay in Tokyo, I accompanied Dr Motoyama and his wife to a conference in the Philippines. Dr Motoyama was to meet with many of the then notorious psychic surgeons and to deliver a paper on his research into the mechanisms of healing. At this time, in the mid 1970s, the psychic surgeons of the Philippines were the subject of much discussion and scientific curiosity, due mainly to reports that during their healing sessions materialisation, dematerialisation and apport phenomena were taking place. According to yoga theory, these are the kind of abilities that accompany the activity of the heart chakra.

We took an early prototype of the AMI machine and tested both healers and patients before, during and after healing sessions. The very clear pattern which emerged from our findings was that the healers had remarkably high levels of energy within the heart and heart protector meridians, and that the patients undergoing healing would often show a marked increase of spleen meridian energy directly after a healing session.

These results bore out the ideas that the manipura chakra is capable of receiving energy and the anahata chakra transmits energy. The heart meridian emerges at the little finger, the heart protector at the middle finger, and we also observed that these fingers were usually used to make 'incisions' into the body. We have seen that in traditional Indian theory, the heart centre is linked with the hands and also with the sense of touch. The healer Tony Agpaoa demonstrated to the conference that he could cut through several layers of surgical tape with the energy emitted from his little finger.

When I first visited the healers in the Philippines many of them were living simple lives within local communities. They carried out their healing work within local churches, which taught a mixture of Catholicism and old shamanism or witchcraft. The healers were without exception simple village people, who from an early age had shown themselves to be gifted in trance and mediumship. They worked with and were directed by spirit guides and, when questioned, could give little information about their work. They did as they were instructed. As they worked with their hands objects would appear, in the early days a piece of wood or glass or another kind of everyday object that was thought to have been part of a spell against the victim. But later 'blood' appeared during the healing sessions, and occasionally pieces of tissue. One of the most interesting discoveries made by researchers in the 1960s was that the type of substance to materialise seemed to depend on the belief system of the patient. Western or more educated patients would cause the materialisation of blood and tissue. Whereas the more primitive villagers would cause the materialisation of sticks and stones or other items associated with spells and witchcraft. In a famous interview Tony Agpaoa revealed a conversation with a spirit guide in which Agpaoa begged that there be no more blood as it made him feel ill. His spirit guide answered that, 'there must be blood in order for them to believe.'

By the mid-1970s the Filipino healers were receiving thousands of visitors from all over the world who had heard stories of their 'miracles'. Whereas many had worked for no return, a condition laid down by many mediumistic healing practices, they now received gifts of money from their comparatively wealthy patients, who were only too happy to donate what they could.

During my first visit the situation amongst the healers was varied, and most seemed to be doing genuine work. Some still worked in comparative obscurity in small local churches with a mainly local population, others had built healing centres to attempt to cope with the ever increasing demand from visitors. Tony Agpaoa had recently constructed his own church with money donated by a local politician. By that time little actual psychic surgery was taking place, though reports from earlier researchers claimed that in the 1960s the healers made actual insicions into the body with their hands. There was certainly a lot of blood, and a lot of tissue, which slowly materialised in the hand of the healer and was then discarded into a bucket below the healing couch. Many researchers took away samples of blood and tissue to be tested in their laboratories back home, in some cases the material did not test out to be of human origin. In some cases the samples had dematerialised before they reached the laboratory. Experiments carried out in the mid-1960s by Dr Motoyama and a group of research scientists did include a specimen which tested out to be from the patient undergoing the surgery.

The healers became the centre of much controversy concerning deception and sleight of hand. They were the subject of many so-called documentaries which 'proved' the whole phenomenon to be a fake. Psychic surgery became the focus of so much interest because according to our accepted world view these things cannot happen. Such events challenge our view of reality and many of us will do all that we can to keep that view of reality intact. By the late '70s the psychic surgery of the Philippines was probably a mixture of true and false, sincerity and deception.

When I returned in 1978 the situation was quite different from that of my first visit. A new healing centre was guarded by gunmen. The benevolent atmosphere had given way to one of suspicion. But this was just one case amongst many. With their new wealth many of the healers succumbed to the problems that money and power can bring. They were unprepared for their sudden exposure to the ways of the West and, as with many primitive peoples, they struggled. The demands on their time and energy were massive, and the attacks by the Western media were cruel, many claiming that all the healers were frauds set up by the government of the Philippines to increase tourism!

In his presentation to the conference, Dr Motoyama explained his ideas on the mechanisms of healing which, in the case of psychic surgery and materialisation, involved the energy of a higher dimension being transformed within the heart chakra and emitted through the hands of the healer. Materialisation of this kind only seems to occur in a mediumistic state.

The heart centre is located at the centre of the seven chakras, and is sometimes said to mediate between the three lower centres and the three upper centres. It is the centre of balance. Swami Satyananda suggests that the realm of the anahata or heart chakra is above the limitations of the physical dimension. Whereas the three lower centres are restricted by the laws of cause and effect, the anahata chakra is not restricted in this way. In traditional Indian philosophy, once the awakening of the anahata chakra has been attained one is able to manipulate physical reality. As the anahata controls the sense of touch, it is often by the sense of touch that these abilities are illustrated – in various paranormal phenomena such as hand healing and telekinesis.

Because of the power associated with the heart centre, its awakening would traditionally require strict teachings concerning correct thinking and judgement. If linked with misplaced ideologies, negativity or pessimism, the power may be damaging, both to the individual and to others. It is love and compassion, together with constant optimism, that must be cultivated in order to correctly use the gifts of the heart centre. Compassion means to feel with others. And as the heart centre awakens, the division between self and other is blurred. True compassion is not something that is attempted in the mind. If you feel with others, you will not harm others. If you feel with the whole world, you will not harm the world. As the individual ego recedes the division between the self and the rest of creation begins to be less solid.

Swami Satyananda says that during the awakening of the heart chakra, the being is in a very delicate situation, suspended almost between one world and the next. The teachings of kundalini yoga suggest that the power of kundalini may rise and fall through the sushumna nadi many times but once it reaches the heart chakra it remains. Should it reach the heart chakra and then descend, it is extremely difficult to raise it again. Again, according to Satyananda, the main reasons for this descent are negativity, pessimism and abuse of power.

Clinical Observations

Although the above are quite extreme examples of the energetic tendencies of these three particular types, they are able to give us a clear picture of the links and relationships between the chakras and the acupuncture meridian system and accompanying imbalances and abilities. The classification of these three main types became the basis of further work and research within the Institute in Tokyo, and it was observed that most people would show a tendency towards one or another of the three. Within my clinical practice I have found these classifications to be useful when attempting to assess the energetic imbalances within an individual, and further clarification can be made when comparing the activity within these three chakras with what are known as the three heaters or three burning spaces in Chinese medicine. These were briefly mentioned as housing the different types of qi, and promoting their functions of defence, nutrition and circulation. The lower heater controls the area of the lower abdomen and the function of water metabolism, defence and fertility, the middle heater controls the upper abdomen and the functions of digestion and assimilation, and the upper heater controls the chest and the function of obtaining oxygen from the breath, generating the rhythmic beating of the heart and the circulation throughout the system of communication (Plate 23).

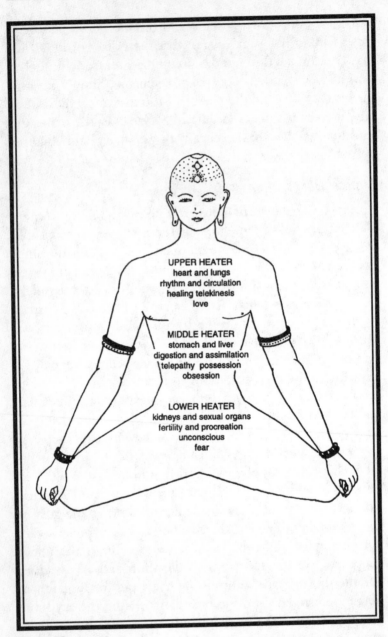

Plate 23

When taking the pulse in three positions on the wrist, an Oriental medicine practitioner is assessing the relative strengths of energy in the three heaters. An even pulse picture will suggest a good balance, but very often one centre is overactive, another underactive. Acupuncture treatment is often aimed to create balance between the three burning spaces. Further information will be gained from assessing the difference in the corresponding pulse positions on the left and right wrist. This may show instability within a particular centre. In Oriental medical terms this may be described as a balance between yin and yang, blood and qi but, according to Dr Motoyama, may also suggest an imbalance between the ida and pingala nadi, and the sympathetic and parasympathetic nervous system. These two aspects of the autonomic nervous system, which control involuntary activity, have the effect of balancing each other in a kind of haemostatic feedback loop. Where the sympathetic nerves contract, the parasympathetic relax; where the sympathetic nerves speed up, the parasympathetic slow down. But whereas the sympathetic nerves accelerate the heart, they slow down the gut. The parasympathetic nerves will slow the heart rate and speed up the movement of the gut. The actions of the sympathetic nervous system tend to prepare the body for emergencies – the so-called fight or flight mechanism. It is interesting to note that in this situation the digestive function is reduced. We know that many digestive problems are stress related, and that hectic modern life can often mean that the organism is in perpetual emergency mode.

It is also interesting to note that the contractions of the anus and the bladder are controlled by the autonomic nervous system. Although we consider these functions to be under our conscious control, it is a control that has to be learnt. Other animals cannot usually control evacuation, and the few that do so tend to be taught by us. This would also suggest that other functions of this system may be brought under conscious control by training, and it is now recognised by science that the peristalsis of the gut and the beating of the heart can be brought under conscious control by strict training. This of course is how Indian yogis are able to survive when buried alive for several days on end.

The sympathetic and parasympathetic aspects of the autonomic nervous system certainly display many similarities to the traditional Chinese descriptions of the way yin and yang function within the body. But this is just one example of the kind of regulation and balance that the Chinese are referring to within the yin/yang hypothesis.

Acupuncture tradition teaches that a weakness in the lower radial pulse position, corresponding to the lower heater, points to a lack of energy in the kidney and bladder meridians, and also a lack of fire at the gate of destiny. Further, an imbalance of yin and yang within the lower heater, indicated for example by a strong pulse on the left and a weak pulse on the right, may suggest a preponderance of the watery aspect of the kidneys to the detriment of the transformative fire. Clinically many problems with fertility show these kinds of imbalance. Fertility demands a balance between the nutritive and holding power of the earth and the generative power of heaven.

A lack of fire or yang in the lower heater may lead to severe energy depletion, and an inability to create defensive qi, to the detriment of the immune system. The fire of the gate of destiny must be kept alive and this part of the body must be kept warm. The Japanese often wear a haramaki, a roll of woollen cloth worn around the lower belly to guard this precious energy. The Chinese practise daily exercise to keep this area warm, energised and functioning well.

Imbalance within the lower heater may also suggest fear and insecurity, or a lack of grounding. There may be emotional instability, and the need to possess as a means to provide security. Working energetically to improve stability and to release blockages caused by old trauma can do much to resolve emotional instability.

Weakness or imbalance within the middle heater will be detected through the pulses of the spleen and stomach, liver and gall bladder, in the central position on the wrist. Here there is an obvious relationship with the digestive system. The original qi, as an agent of the gate of destiny, assists in the breakdown and assimilation of food. A left/right imbalance will often mean that the subtle processes of absorption and assimilation aided by the spleen (and pancreas) are dominated by the overactivity of the liver. Within the inner organs, the spleen is traditionally a yin organ, whereas the liver has a tendency to overactivity and yang. We have seen that within the autonomic nervous system, the sympathetic nerves which react to stress also have the effect of slowing down the digestion of food. Overactivity of the yang aspect of the liver, commonly seen in clinic as a result of stress, will have a detrimental effect on the spleen's ability to absorb and transform. Depending on the individual case this may have the effect of weight loss or weight gain, or simply erratic digestion as seen in many cases of what is generally labelled irritable bowel syndrome.

Acupuncture theory teaches that the emotion associated with spleen dysfunction is overthinking – the action of turning thoughts around and around in the head. The result is the knotting of qi, which creates an energetic blockage between the upper and lower heaters. We are all familiar with the kind of knotted feeling that can sit in the pit of the stomach, creating tension in the diaphragm and interfering with breathing patterns. The earth element associated with the digestive function acts as an intermediary between the elements of water and fire. Blockage within the middle heater will create a lack of communication between the lower and upper heaters. In treatment it is often this communication which needs to be restored.

We have also seen that the spleen is concerned with the reception and assimilation of ideas. A weakness of the spleen or an imbalance in the manipura chakra may result in a lack of discrimination in the reception of ideas, or a lack of protection from the thoughts and ideas of others. On the other hand there may be cold detachment, or even ruthlessness and a need to control, as a wall of protection is built between the self and others.

The energy of the upper heater, related to the heart and the lungs, is detected at the upper radial pulse, closest to the wrist. Observation of the rhythm of the breath and the speed of the pulse will also help to ascertain the relative energetic functions of the heart and lungs. The upper heater contains the upper sea of qi, and it is from here that the qi energy is said to begin its circulation throughout the meridian system. It is the centre of all communication. We have seen that healing energy is projected outwards from the heart centre, and there is evidence that some healers may over-use this centre and eventually suffer from heart problems. Similarly clairvoyants who receive information through the manipura chakra will often suffer from digestive problems through over-use of the centre. Humility is said to be the protector of the heart, and this includes the understanding that we cannot do everything, that we cannot give constantly of ourselves, unless we are able to do that without a shadow of resentment.

In traditional Chinese medicine, the emotions connected to the heart and lungs are joy and grief. They are most adversely affected by pessimism and negativity. The energy of this centre is adversely affected by emotional attachment. So many cases of asthma late in life have come from the inability to face life after the death of a loved one. In other cases there may be an inability to show grief, a suppression of feelings which eventually emerge as a physical problem. It is important to grieve, but in time we must learn to move on. We cannot experience joy by clinging to the past but by being open and allowing life to move through us. Not to hold on to emotions, not to store up past grief, but to perceive life as a constantly changing pattern of experience.

As we move on to the next section of the book, we will look at ways to work with these centres. We will learn simple exercises and meditation practices to bring balance, to calm and to energise. They are based on the practices that I learned in Japan and observed in action daily. Added to the common sense approach to diet and sleep, the body is able to find its own natural balance and inclination.

Part Three
Practical Transformation

Returning to one's roots is known as stillness
This is what is meant by returning to one's destiny.

Lao zi, XVI

The theory of Chinese medicine and Indian yoga is complex and at times quite difficult to grasp. The difficulty often lies in the strange terminology and the different way of viewing the body. The practice, on the contrary, tends to be very simple. So simple that we may sometimes feel that we are not really doing much at all! We are used to exercising our muscles and joints but when practising yoga, tai ji, or any of the other Oriental disciplines, it is helpful to remember that we are working with our vital energy – our qi, our prana – which implies that we are working on the intermediary level between the physical and the subtle, between the mind and the body. Any work that we do while concentrating the mind and engaging the breath has the power to make change on the physical, mental and emotional level. As these levels of our being become aligned with our intended pattern, we begin to feel in balance, our spirits begin to shine.

It may also be useful to remember that Eastern therapy focuses on health, whereas Western medicine tends to focus on disease. If someone comes to see me for acupuncture treatment, I may ask about the problem or 'pattern of disharmony', but that will not be the focus of my treatment. The focus of the treatment will be on restoring harmony

135

and balance. It is therefore not necessary to label the disease or dysfunction, but to have a clear picture of the intended pattern of harmony.

It is the same with exercise. If we perform exercises which are intended to restore the natural balance of the energy in the body, any imperfections will eventually be brought into harmony. It may take time, and sometimes a bit of extra help and guidance is needed, but the idea is to remind the body/mind of its possible state of perfection.

As Eastern forms of exercise became more widely known in the West they have been taken up by many as a good way to keep the body in shape or to combat stress. For that they are no doubt effective, but it is not their sole intention. A fashionably perfect body has very little to do with good health, and even less to do with emotional and mental stability. Our perfection is individual to us, and may not conform to the current trend. We must essentially begin with who we are and where we are. We can no more take the path of another than we can assume their physical body. We need to feel good; feel at ease in our bodies, so that our spirits are able to manifest unencumbered by bodily restraints. Even if the body has a disability, we can still help the qi to function well. Within the Eastern traditions, the health and strength of the physical body tends to be seen as a preparation for the more advanced practice of working with the breath and concentrating the mind, the aim being to transform our lives not merely to gain a perfect shape.

So how do these exercises actually help in the process of transformation? Once again we need to remember that we are working with subtle energy and that we are therefore working with the interface between mind and body. If I use an acupuncture needle to stimulate qi, the effect may be felt physically or it may be felt emotionally. I have personally experienced and witnessed many times the emotional release that may occur with the stimulation of subtle energy. We are talking about restoring flow and restoring balance. Blockages to that movement of freeflow may occur at any point on the matter/energy continuum. Usually they manifest on both levels simultaneously.

Working with the energy channels and energy centres we aim to balance the subtle energy system. Using simple methods of movement and concentration, we can help the body/mind to break out of destructive patterns of behaviour and to be open to the constant possibility of change and transformation. We do not necessarily want to impose new patterns, just to align with what is natural; and that means what is natural for us as an individual, not to align to some externally imposed norm. As we come closer to what is natural for us, mentally, emotionally and physically, we come closer to our true nature. We come closer to our true nature by letting go of patterns of behaviour – behaviour of mind and body – that are not truly our own. They do not lead us towards health and wholeness. Becoming ourselves is a process of letting go.

Many of the practices within Chinese medicine, and more specifically Chinese yoga, aim to put us back in touch with our source, allowing us to align with our personal destiny; to be healthy in the deepest sense, in which our emotional and spiritual health is seen as the basis of our physical health. The exercises of Indian yoga aim to align the body, to purify the subtle energy channels, and to balance the energy centres.

The very process of creating balance may at times bring instability as we shift from one state to another, one mode of operation to the next. But each symptom is understood as a teacher for the next stage of our path. We must constantly ask, what can I learn from this? What part of my life is deviating from the pattern of my origin? Where am I missing the opportunity to align with my true nature? And all the time we continue to keep the channels open; open to change, open to light, open to spirit.

The Exercises

The exercises that follow are drawn from both the Chinese and the Indian systems. It is my hope to demystify some of the more obscure terminology, to explain this with simple examples of the theory made practice. Some of the exercises involve movement, some are performed standing or sitting quite still. All of the exercises involve the breath and the concentration.

When I look back to my first introduction to breathing exercises in Japan I remember a small room at the back of a small Zen temple full of local Tokyo people. We sat and learned to control our breathing for a couple of hours every Saturday afternoon. Then we went our own way and got on with our chores. It was not until I had pneumonia many years later and lost the natural rhythm of my breath that I truly appreciated the value of what I had learned. Within my clinical practice and within my everyday life I constantly stress the importance of the breath. Maybe I had to lose my own in order to truly understand this.

I have seen a greater degree of transformation in patients from the adoption of simple breathing exercises than from years of acupuncture treatment. And that is not to say that acupuncture is ineffective – but when individuals take their destiny into their own hands and decide to work directly with their own energy the effect is always extraordinary.

If we stretch our bodies once a day, gradually the spine begins to be more erect, the internal organs are strengthened, the energy begins to flow. If we practise concentration and awareness for just a few minutes each week, gradually concentration and awareness become part of our lives. Like water running over a stone, simple repeated actions make permanent change.

'Sitting still and doing nothing' may be the highest aim of the Daoist sages, but for many of us it is difficult to sit and concentrate on our breath, our minds are busy and difficult to tame. Many Zen teachings liken the mind to a horde of chattering monkeys – almost impossible to control. Qi gong exercises are specifically designed to work with the breath and the concentration with the aid of simple movements, each movement aiding the flow of energy through the subtle network of channels. With practice the physical movement can become less, as the imagination and concentration take over in guiding the energy and the breath. In this first section we will look at some basic qi gong exercises to circulate the energy, to balance yin and yang, heaven and earth. We will look at practices for the circulation of light, or 'turning the light around', in the primary yin and yang channels, as well as other basic balancing breathing techniques.

In the second section we will concentrate on traditional Indian yoga exercises to strengthen the spine and to correct misalignments within the spinal column. Breathing exercises from the yoga tradition for clearing the energy channels and for balancing the ida and pingala nadis will also be introduced in this section.

In the third section we will look at the three major energy centres and draw on both the Chinese and Indian traditions for specific ways to work with them.

The combination of Indian and Chinese techniques often provides a good balance. The strengthening effects of yoga asana can be balanced by the softening effects of qi gong. The extensive knowledge of the subtle energy system of channels and points within Chinese medicine can be augmented by in-depth knowledge of the energy centres in the Indian tradition. In Japan there has always been a tendency to take the best from other cultures and refine and modify, and while I was studying in Japan in the 1970s there were quite a few avant-garde individuals who were teaching an interesting combination of yoga asana and traditional meridian therapy. Shiatsu schools were incorporating yoga postures into their teaching of meridian exercises. A combination of different methods can produce an effective practice.

But not everything that follows here will appeal to everyone. It is important for each individual to find a practice which suits them and which they enjoy. As a simple guide, always include some basic balancing techniques and spinal stretches. At the beginning just stick to these two sections without working on any specific area - in fact an effective practice could be made from any of the individual exercises in these first two sections. Strength often lies in simplicity. Try to do too much and you may become discouraged. So let us begin with some simple qi gong.

Qi Gong and Daoist Yoga

Qi gong translates as energy work. The aim of the exercises is to stimulate the flow of energy in the meridians, to balance and harmonise the entire subtle energy system. The exercises are usually performed from the standing position, with the knees slightly bent and the spine straight. It is worth spending some time getting used to standing quite still in this way before continuing with the movements.

Basic Position:

Stand with the feet parallel and facing forwards, hip-width apart. Place the hands on the hips and slightly bend the knees, making sure that they are directly above the toes. Feel the hip bones to make sure that they are level. Making these simple adjustments begins to focus our attention on the structure of the body. We often have slight imbalances in the way that we stand, which may reflect old injuries or illnesses which have made us use one side of the body more than the other. Or it may simply be habit. Carrying a heavy bag every day on the same shoulder, for example, will eventually distort the spine and the hips. Taking a few minutes to align the body, to feel where we tend to hold ourselves in imbalance is the first step to self-awareness.

Sway backwards and forwards on the feet to find a good stable position. The weight should be quite even between the back and front, the inside and outside of each foot, and evenly spread between the two feet.

Stretch out the curve in the lower spine by bringing the tailbone down and forwards. The area above the pubic bone will soften and relax and move in towards the centre of the body. The hands on your hip bones will be moved slightly backwards. This movement is subtle but will help to extend the spine and create more grounding and balance. Once you feel comfortable in this position, let the hands fall naturally to the sides.

The kidney meridian, responsible for grounding and stability, has its origin in the sole of the foot, and is often said to draw energy directly from the earth. While standing in the basic qi gong position, imagine that the body is rooted through the soles of the feet deeply into the ground. Stand tall and straight imagining that you have grown roots which extend deep into the earth. Your lower body feels solid and strong.

From this base of strength and solidity lengthen and straighten the spine. Imagine that the top of the head is gently pulled upwards, extending the space between each vertebra, keeping the knees relaxed and slightly bent. You may remember the image of the pole star as the great ridgepole (tai

Fig 1

Fig 2

Fig 3

ji) of the universe, holding everything in its place, and imagine yourself suspended by this force of the heavens (Fig. 1).

As the lower body retains its strength and stability, the upper body becomes loose and light. Stand in this position breathing deeply and evenly for a few minutes. Then relax and shake the limbs loosely, as if you are shaking excess water from the fingers and toes.

Warming Up

Before you begin any form of exercise, take a few moments to stretch and release the body. With the feet shoulder-width apart and parallel, stretch up with the hands above the head. Reach out with the hands and fully extend the spine; imagine that the fingertips are stretching up to heaven, contacting the yang energy source of the galaxy. Take a few deep breaths in and out while enjoying the stretch (Fig. 2).

Then release and allow the body to fall forwards naturally, bringing the hands to the ground. Bend the knees and be comfortable and relaxed. Allow the hands to contact the earth. Imagine the cooling, nourishing energy of the earth being drawn up into your body, bringing stability and calm (Fig. 3).

After a few stretches, shake first the arms and then the legs. Rotate the shoulders to get rid of any tension.

Balancing the Lower and Upper Seas of Qi

This is one of the simplest moving qi gong practices, which is often used as a warm up for tai ji. Once you have mastered the movements and co-ordinated the rhythm of the breath, you will feel as if the hands are being moved by the breath, the breath being moved by the hands.

Method:

1   Stand in the basic position, take some time to feel your way into balance and stability. Take a few deep breaths.

2 With an in-breath, slowly raise the hands to chest level, elbows bent, palms facing upwards (Fig. 4). Feel as if you are guiding the breath with the hands.

3 Turn the palms and move the hands slowly downwards as you breathe out (Fig. 5).

4 As you reach the level of the lower abdomen, turn the palms again and raise the hands as you inhale.

Repeat 3 and 4. Allow your breath to find its own rhythm, relax the arms and hands so that they are able to be moved by the breath. Expand as you inhale, sink down as you exhale.

Try to keep the exercise going for five minutes. If you stop, gently shake the limbs to get rid of any tension and begin again. Remember to keep the knees and shoulders relaxed. Bring the exercise to an end by gradually reducing the movement. As hand movements become smaller and smaller, imagine that you are collecting energy between your hands until you have a small ball of energy between them. Finally place your hands over the lower abdomen. Remain still for a few moments as the energy continues to circulate. When you feel completely still, shake the limbs to release any accumulated tension.

Effects:

This continual movement of the hands and the breath between the lower sea of qi in the lower abdomen and the upper sea of qi in the chest creates a balance between the lower and middle dan tian – the sexual centre and the heart centre. The movement of the arms in rhythm with the breath allows the chest to expand, and the diaphragm to relax. As a basic balancing exercise it the most simple and the most effective.

So often the diaphragm is an area of tension and potential energy blockage, which can create digestive problems as well as palpitations and anxiety. As we saw when we looked at the circulation within the basic yin and yang channels, the gate at the level of the diaphragm filters the energy to ensure that only the purest is allowed into the region of the lungs and the heart. Deep breathing helps to release tension and obstruction around the diaphragm, and also helps to create a healthy rhythm for the heart and lungs. The regular rhythmic movement of the arms adds to this expansion and contraction and also energises the meridians of the heart and lungs which flow from deep within the chest to the fingertips.

As you progress with this exercise the hands will begin to feel energised. Bring your attention to the centre of the palm of the hand where the heart meridian flows. Awareness of this area helps us to develop sensitivity in the hands, which in the Oriental tradition are used for diagnosis on the body (receiving information/energy) as well as for hand healing (giving information/energy). The heart meridian in the palm of the hand and the kidney meridian in the sole of the foot are the two key points of reference throughout the practice of qi gong. An awareness of these points helps us to tune in to the yin energy which is drawn up and returned to the earth through the feet, and the yang energy drawn from heaven through the fingertips and returned through the palm of the hand (Figs. 6 and 7).

The kidney meridian has the most direct link with the lower sea of qi, with reproductive energy and sexuality. This lower sea of qi is our rooting in the world and our ability to function in the real world with our feet planted securely on the ground. It is also the root of our ability to transform. Unless we are rooted in reality, all our ideas, thoughts,

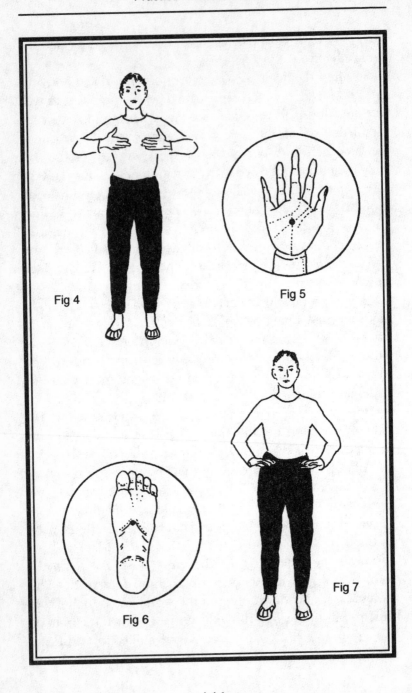

Fig 4

Fig 5

Fig 6

Fig 7

emotions, passions are unable to have a true effect on our lives. They are unable to bring about change. Real change occurs when the lower sea of qi and the upper sea of qi are in communication; when the stabilising energy of the water element and the transformative energy of fire are brought together. The heart meridian is the 'emperor fire' – the purest fire energy, the kidney meridian, the water; together these two meridians make up the shao yin, or lesser yin energy circulation, which controls the most inner, the most precious aspects of our being. The kidneys store the essence, the heart is the home of the spirit. The harmonising and balancing of essence and spirit is the key to health and transformation.

Most of the exercises will also address this balance, but this is the simplest, the most basic and possibly the most effective way to begin.

Balancing the Three Dan Tian

The last exercise can be extended to balance the three dan tian, in a movement which follows the pathways of the primary yin and yang channels.

Preparation:

Assume the basic qi gong stance. Bring awareness to the soles of the feet and the palms of the hands. Place the hands over the abdomen just below the navel and relax. As you extend the lower spine and tuck the tailbone into the body you will feel a slight contraction in the lower abdomen. Try to become aware of the feeling and keep it throughout the practice.

Method:

1 Slowly separate the hands, and with an in-breath bring the hands up to the chest and over the top of the head; the elbows will bend naturally (Fig. 8).

2 As you breathe out the hands trace the back of the head, over the shoulders and back to the lower abdomen (Fig. 9).

3 Turn the hands upwards and begin the movement again, keeping in rhythm with the breath.

As you perform the simple movements, focus your mind on the primary yin and yang channels. With the in-breath, imagine the energy flowing up the front of the body, over the abdomen, through the heart, the throat and into the brow centre. With the out-breath, imagine the breath circulating over the back of the head and down the spine (Fig. 10).

Continue for at least ten complete cycles, then gradually bring the movement back to the centre by completing three of the breaths while moving the hands between the abdomen and the chest. Continue to reduce the movement and finally bring the hands to rest on the lower abdomen.

Remain still for a few moments, reconnecting with the centre in the lower abdomen and with the soles of the feet. When your breath is even and your body quite still, shake the limbs, move the shoulders and relax.

Effects:

This exercise will balance the yin and yang channels and the three energy fields, the lower, middle and upper dan tian. Most meditations using the primary yin and yang channels visualise the energy or light flowing up the spine and down the front of the body, and we will go into more detail with that later. This particular method activates the yin energy and is particularly calming and stabilising.

Some of the more recent investigations at the Institute for Human Sciences, Tokyo, have suggested that the natural flow of energy within the primary yin and yang channels is

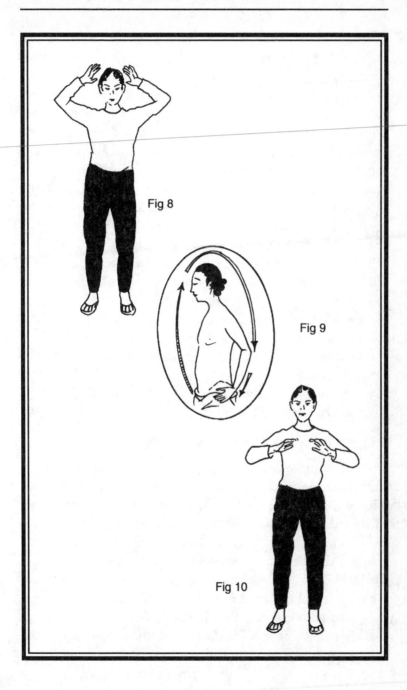

Fig 8

Fig 9

Fig 10

potentially different in men and women. Although the energy can flow in either direction, the tendency is for a flow up the spine and down the front of the body in men, and a flow up the front of the body and down the spine in women. According to Chinese medical theory, the yang energy within the spinal channels brings light and clarity to the brain and to the upper orifices. The yin channel brings moisture, and the richness of the essences. At menopause, for example, the yin of the kidneys may become deficient, the face becomes dry and begins to wrinkle, the eyes may be blurred and lacking in moisture. At this time an exercise to increase the yin in the upper part of the body would be very beneficial. Imagine the yin washing over the head and face as you practise, drawing from the deep sources within the earth.

As the hands reach the top of the head, they contact the yang energy which is drawn over the head and down the back, completing the circuit in the lower abdomen. Although the hands move along the front of the body, the imagination should remain on the back. Any exercise on the front and back energy channels will balance the energy. The exercise is particularly balancing and calming.

Balancing Yin and Yang, Heaven and Earth

The third balancing exercise takes the movement even further, giving the body a full extension and a full relaxation. The hands describe the flow of energy throughout the body of the main meridians, the yin ascending from the earth, up the inner legs, over the front of the abdomen and chest and through the inner arms to the fingertips. Describing an arc, the hands gather in the yang energy of the cosmos, reaching high above the head and moving over the shoulders, through the back and down over the kidneys and the back of the legs. This full movement also follows the movement of the yin and yang qiao mai, the fifth and sixth of the eight extraordinary meridians, whose function is to balance yin and yang within the body.

Method:

1 From the basic qi gong position, place the hands over the abdomen, breathing calmly and deeply (Fig. 11).

2 When the body feels balanced, the breath even, bring the hands away from the abdomen, and with the fingertips pointing to the centre midline, begin to move the hands to the chest as you breathe in (Fig. 12).

3 With an out-breath extend the hands horizontally, finally stretching into the fingertips (Fig. 13).

4 As you breathe in, stretch the arms high above the head describing an arc (Fig. 14).

5 Breathe out, allowing the elbows to bend and the hands to move over the back of the head and shoulders, and along the front midline of the body, until they come to rest at the back of the waist over the kidneys. Inhale (Figs 15, 16, 17).

6 As you exhale, bend down to make contact with the earth, brushing the backs of the legs (Figs 18, 19).

7 Relax for a few breaths before you inhale, moving the hands along the inside of the legs and bring them to rest on the abdomen (Fig. 20).

Repeat in your own time. The movements may be done quickly or slowly and the breathing will change according to your speed and intention. The breath should be natural at all times – do not hold the breath or lengthen the breath in any

Fig 11

Fig 12

Fig 13

Fig 14

Fig 15

Fig 16

Fig 17

Fig 18

Fig 19

Fig 20

way that is uncomfortable. Done very quickly, the exercise can be used to stimulate energy flow in the meridians. It is possible to use quick, brushing strokes, with the complete upward movement accompanying the in-breath, the downward movement the out-breath. This acts as a kind of cleansing of the energy field, brushing off debris and accumulated dust. A kind of energy spring clean!

Balancing Heaven and Earth was introduced as a basic qi gong exercise in my previous book, *Reclaiming the Wisdom of the Body*, and forms the basis of much qi gong practice. Done with awareness and concentration, it can become a powerful tool for self-healing. Once you are very familiar with the movements, it is interesting to perform this exercise very slowly. Gradually slow the pace until the breathing is quite calm, the hands contacting the energy field around the body. Moving very slowly and with awareness, you may be able to detect areas of the body where the energy field seems to be particularly weak, or areas where the hands seem to 'stick'. Remain in a particular position, using the hands in sweeping, cleaning movements, until it feels freer. It takes time to tune in to this kind of energy exercise, but it is good training for the hands and for the concentration. But be light with it. If you do not feel anything, that is fine. Carry on with the more physical movement and try again another day.

Energy Exercise

To get your hands used to feeling energy, hold them shoulder-width apart, with palms facing, and slowly, with concentration and awareness, bring the hands closer together. Repeat this a few times and you will begin to feel a resistance between the two palms as they come closer. Play with the feeling. Some days it will be stronger than others. Sometimes you will be able to concentrate more easily than others. All this is fine (Fig. 21).

Standing Meditation for the Lower Dan Tian

Much of qi gong exercise is standing meditation. The position of the body and the hands and the focus of the mind bring the attention to a particular area of the energy body. The palms of the hands are aligned with the area of concentration, and the imagination directs the energy from the palm of the hand. Here we are giving instructions for concentration to the lower dan tian, which is the most usual form of standing meditation. But you can direct the qi with your hands to the area of digestion, or to the heart, or simply relax and concentrate on the centre between the eyebrows. If, for example, the mind is feeling sluggish and you need more focus and concentration, choose to concentrate on the upper dan tian; if on the other hand you are in need of physical stability, concentrate to the lower dan tian. If you are in need of emotional stability, focus on the middle dan tian.

1   Stand in the basic qi gong position, taking care that the feet are evenly contacting the ground. Sway backwards and forwards and from side to side to ensure that your balance is good. Sink down into the feet with the knees bent. Swing from side to side with loose arms, allowing them to completely relax and release. During these exercises there may be a build-up of tension in the arms and shoulders, so check from time to time to make sure that the shoulders are relaxed. With your mind, let go of any tension. If at any time during the exercise the tension becomes unbearable, lower the arms and shake them gently before taking up the position again.

2   Allow the arms to come to rest at the side of your hips. Take a few deep breaths and raise the arms until the palms

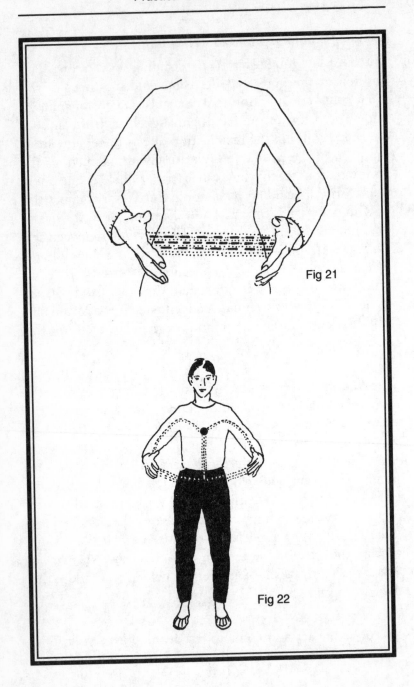

Fig 21

Fig 22

are level with the lower abdomen and facing the area mid-way between the pubic bone and the navel. The arms describe a circle in front of the body, as if you are holding a large ball. With a deep exhalation, allow the awareness to move down to the lower dan tian. Lightly close your eyes. Feel rooted into the feet, and allow the breath to expand the abdomen as you breathe in, slightly contract the abdomen as you breathe out. Imagine that the breath is expelled from the chest into the arms and redirected through the palms of the hands back to the abdomen. Visualise this circuit of energy for a few breaths, until you feel the pattern is established, then gently focus the attention to the lower dan tian, watching the rise and fall with the inhalation and exhalation of the breath. Be light. Allow the arms to be light in their sockets, the head and spine lightly suspended by a thread from heaven. Do not force the concentration; keep the brow relaxed, the chest open, the shoulders dropped (Fig. 22).

It is surprisingly difficult to stand still. All kinds of aches and pains vie for our attention. But try not to give them too much of your awareness. Consciously relax and release. Try not to drop the arms until you have tried to work with your awareness to release the pain. If you do have to move, keep the feet secure, shake the hands and rotate the shoulders, then continue. You will find that with practice you can hold the position for longer. If standing still is just not for you, stick to the moving exercises, and just stand for a short time after you have completed.

To conclude, slowly bring the hands to rest over the lower abdomen. After a few moments open your eyes and release your concentration. Shake your hands, shake your feet, and jump up and down a few times, shaking the whole body. Bring your hands to the back of your waist and rub your kidneys vigorously for a few moments, then relax.

Turning the Light Around

The circulation of light, or turning the light around, is the central meditation practice within Daoist yoga. It has a very similar function to the qi gong exercises above, but is practised simply with the imagination, breath and concentration with no actual movement. Our study of the Daoist body map has given us much information for the imagination to work with, and we can use the map as a guide to our concentration in the early stages if it is useful.

This exercise is practised from the sitting position. There are many possible variations of posture, but it is important that the spine is straight, with a good lift upwards especially in the lower lumbar vertebrae. The extension of the lower spine is much more important than the position of the legs, so if it is difficult to keep the lift while sitting on the floor, use a firm cushion or sit on a chair.

The Sitting Positions:

1 Sit on a small firm cushion with the legs extended in front of you. Bend the right leg and bring the foot to the groin, placing the heel against the perineum and the foot against the upper thigh. Bend the other leg and bring the foot on top of the right calf, tucking the toes in. The heels should be aligned. Straighten the spine and let the knees rest on the floor. It is important to feel solidly grounded on the floor. If there is any discomfort or shakiness, try a higher pad or change position (Fig. 23).

If this is possible, place the lower heel under the perineum, exerting a slight pressure between the scrotum and the anus for men, or at the base of the vagina for women. This is the external point of intersection of the yin and yang primary channels. An awareness of this point during the meditation aids the focus of attention, and gives a point of reference for the rising of the energy.

2 Sit on a firm cushion or pad, with the feet pointing backwards. It is easier to keep the lower spine straight in this position, but unless you have a good lift in the spine, it may create discomfort in the legs. The pad needs to be high enough to allow the blood to circulate freely (Fig. 24).

3 Sit on the front of a chair making sure that feet are planted securely on the ground. Be aware of the contact between the feet and the floor. Consciously straighten the spine, extending upwards as you tuck your chin slightly under. If you need to use the support of the chair back, make sure that you can keep your feet firmly on the ground while using the back of the chair to help lift the spine. Work with the chair, and, if necessary, use a block or pad under the feet (Fig. 25).

Method:

The exercise involves imagining light travelling from the base of the spine, through the spinal column and into the head. At the top of the head, the light is turned downwards to the point between and behind the eyebrows. It is then made to descend through the throat to the chest, and through the abdomen until it rests in the lower dan tian. From the abdomen the light is brought down to the perineum to begin another circulation.

In Japan I was taught a simple circulation of the breath, moving up the spine to the brow centre with the in-breath, holding for a few seconds, and down to the lower dan tian with the out-breath. The light is made to descend to the perineum before beginning a new breath. This simple exercise regulates the flow of energy within the primary yin

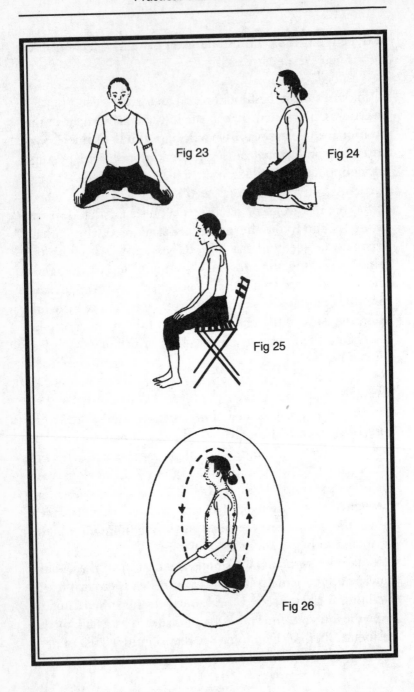

Fig 23

Fig 24

Fig 25

Fig 26

and yang channels. This is the simplest and safest exercise, and if you are new to meditation it is the perfect place to begin. Its effects are always harmonising and balancing, but if practised regularly, the effects are powerful.

Once you are used to the practice, you can bring in your own variations, stopping for example, at each of the gates as you bring the light up the spine, taking a few breaths and imagining the light filling each area. You may decide to pay particular attention to one area where you feel weak or blocked. At the brow centre take a few deep breaths, imagining that you are breathing light in and out of the upper dan tian, filling the entire head and brain with light and energy. As your attention moves down the front channel, stop at the heart centre and take a few deep breaths, filling the area of the heart and lungs with light and energy. Pause again at the lower dan tian, breathing in light and energy to the lower abdomen (Fig. 26).

Later we will go more deeply into concentration on each of the individual energy gates and centres. But let us visualise a journey through this imaginary landscape, trying to familiarise ourselves with the images on the way. If you enjoy this meditation, it may be useful to make your own tape.

Visualisation

Sit with the spine erect, the chin tucked slightly under, extending the back of the neck. Allow the tip of the tongue to curl gently backwards and rest on the upper palate, bringing the awareness to the upper junction of the primary yin and yang channels, and making a bridge between the two, just as the pressure on the perineum brings awareness to the lower convergence. Relax and release any tension in the jaw and throat. The teeth will be slightly apart.

Bring your attention to the lower abdomen, extending

the lower lumbar vertebrae and tucking the tailbone in towards the centre of the body. As you feel a slight tension in the belly, be aware of the point deep within which is the source of the energy channels.

Breathe deeply but gently into the lower abdomen and slowly bring your attention down to the very base of the trunk. Imagine a pool of water accumulating there. At the centre of the perineum, imagine a water wheel, pushing the water from the pool into the lower spine, the children working the wheel, are invigorated by your breath. With each out-breath water gushes from the pool into the spinal channel, passing through the gully formed by the rocks of the sacrum into the stream of the lower spine. This is the first gate, the gate of immortality. Once through the gate the water flows through the lower vertebrae until it reaches the great cauldron of inner alchemy. Water meets fire and becomes vapour in its first alchemical transformation. This is the fire of the gate of destiny, the second gate on the path. Breathe into this area of the lower spine, imagine that your breath acts as a bellows to the fire, create balance between fire and water, adjusting the flow of water to the strength of the fire. Then allow the vapour to rise up the spine through the upper lumbar and lower thoracic vertebrae.

The third gate is at the level of the diaphragm, where the vapour is filtered before it is able to gain access to the area of the heart. Breathe deeply, be aware of the expansion and contraction of the diaphragm, feel the place on the spine directly behind the heart centre and relax and release with each breath. Imagine that the vapour is becoming finer and more subtle as it passes through this gate and into the upper back and neck. At the fourth gate the spine enters the skull, and the subtle energy flows into the head and the brain, bringing lightness and clarity. At the mountain peaks at the top of the head, sits the silent figure of Lao zi. Imagine yourself seated within the mountain peaks, the night sky is clear, and directly overhead is the pole star, holding the universe in balance. Imagine the light of the pole star penetrating the top of your head and mixing with the pure energy that has accumulated in the brain. Breathe in the gentle radiance of the pole star, feel held by its force.

As you breathe, become aware of a point between and behind the eyebrows. With our attention focused on the upper dan tian, we are able to forget the body, to rest for a few moments in the realm of the spirit, beyond the duality of yin and yang, the place of detachment and inner vision. Breathe gently and relax.

From this point between and behind the eyebrows, the centre of the upper dan tian, bring the attention slowly to the back of the mouth, where the tongue gently rests against the soft palate. Here the yin fluid or nectar collects to make its descent through the primary yin channel. This is the heavenly pond, calm and still, reflecting the sky. Imagine the fluid dripping through the throat, cooling, calming and moistening as it flows down towards the heart. Bring this stillness into the heart, aware of our connection with the pole star, and aligning the heart centre to receive the influence of heaven. As you breathe, feel the rhythmic expansion and contraction of the chest. The middle dan tian is the centre of the ancestral qi, which helps to keep the body aligned to its preordained pattern. The lungs are the seat of the po, that aspect of the spirit which controls those automatic functions of the body which are usually out of our conscious control. And all this is dependent on the rhythm of the breath. As you gently breathe in and out, know that you are contacting this energy.

Breathe in deeply and as you breathe out imagine the breath flowing out through the heart centre, and extending as far as you can imagine. From your seat within the peaks of the mountains, breathe in the light of the pole star through the crown of the head and as you breathe out through the heart centre, extend your breath to the furthest horizon.

A calm and open heart is able to experience emotion fully and deeply, but not cling to emotion. Emotions flow freely but do not disturb the calm of the centred heart. Thoughts will come and go but not disturb the centred mind. When the head and heart are aligned there is stillness.

The cool liquid moves through the diaphragm to the digestive organs, calming the solar plexus, and through the navel to rest in the lower dan tian. Here we are back to the origin; back to the undifferentiated oneness before the emergence of life. Breathe into the abdomen, feel the stability of this lower centre, the weight of the buttocks and the legs or the feet on the ground. Feel rooted in the earth, strong and powerful. Allow the feeling of physical stability at your base to give an extra lift to the spine. Be aware of the light of the pole star shining through the crown of the head and descending to the lower dan tian; allow the subtle and physical to merge with the breath; the cool nectar with the fire of the gate of destiny. Then imagine the stream of liquid energy flowing down into the pool at the base of the trunk, strengthening the sexual organs. The pool accumulates, a deep dark pool surrounded by steep rocks of the pelvis, until the breath contacts the water wheel, and the water from the pool begins its ascent once again.

Effects:

All practices which focus the attention on the primary yin and yang channels have the effect of creating balance and harmony within the energy body. The movement of the breath has a cleansing and purifying effect on the energy channels. This in turn affects the function of the nervous system. The spinal nerves are in direct contact with the nerve plexuses which are linked to all the internal organs. Focusing the attention and the breath on the spinal cord helps to balance the sympathetic and parasympathetic nervous system; visualising light flowing through the subtle energy channels within the spine, then bringing the light in the form of nectar back down the front of the body, allows the correct alignment of the energy field, which acts as the blueprint of our material body. We are helping to reinstate the original symmetry of the energy body – a symmetry which we tend to lose with development.

The body reacts well to visualisation, and to the simple repetition of the same movement, the same thought, the same breath. The body is like a child, and we need to re-educate the body in the same way as we would teach a child. With visualisation and use of the imagination, the mind is able to contact the deep functions of the subtle energy system. The imagery is rich in symbolism which provides a tool for the mind, the combination of imagination, concentration and awareness of the breath creates the possibility of developing new and healthy patterns of mind and body. With visualisation and concentration we can begin to understand the mind/body links. We know that they are not separate, but influence each other constantly. To make lasting change in the body it is essential to engage the mind. And in order to bring about real transformation in ourselves and in the world we must truly embody our ideas.

The circulation helps us to understand the importance of aspiring to the mountain tops of spiritual enlightenment, but also of bringing back the fruits of that enlightenment to be embodied in physical reality. It teaches the importance of the cycle, the cycle of growth and decline, birth and death. We can visualise the cycle of the moon: the new moon at the base of the spine, the full moon at the top of the head, the cycle of waxing and waning symbolising the movement of energy from yin to yang, from yang back to yin. No one point in the cycle can be more important than any other, as the whole is always necessary for completion (Fig. 27).

YOGA AND PRANAYAMA

Exercises which activate the subtle energy channels are also found within the Indian yoga tradition, and it is useful to include some of the more physical exercises of hatha yoga into your practice to give more strength and flexibility to the spine. The postures of hatha yoga are intended to align the physical structure but also the energetic structure of the body. Most teachers of hatha yoga will create a class which has a balance of exercises, including strengthening standing poses, backward and forward bends, spinal twists and inversions. In your own practice it is always important to create a similar balance.

The exercises taught within the tradition of both Chinese and Indian yoga place a great emphasis on working with the spinal column. In recent centuries Western medical science has begun to understand the importance of the spinal cord and the spinal nerves as the centre of our physical activity, and the correspondences found in acupuncture show that the Chinese have been aware of these connections for thousands of years. But these ancient Indian and Chinese systems were also aware that both the nervous system and the subtle energy in the spinal cord is the key to our personal and collective evolution; the chakras or energy centres along the spinal cord acting as transmuters of energy from the gross to the more subtle.

It is for working directly with the spine that Indian yoga postures are intended. And traditionally they are a prerequisite for any serious meditation or concentration practices. But even though we may be using more physical movements, it is important to remember that we are still

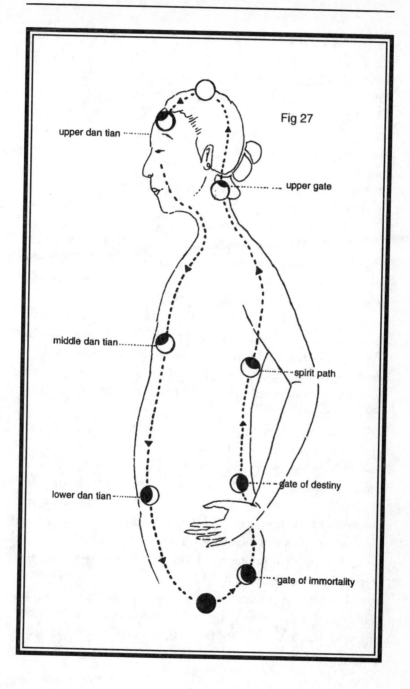

Fig 27

upper dan tian

upper gate

middle dan tian

spirit path

gate of destiny

lower dan tian

gate of immortality

working with subtle energy. Our aim is to create a good flow of energy through the subtle channels within the spinal cord. This flow may be affected by misplaced vertebrae and hatha yoga is the best way both to prevent and correct these problems. To obtain benefits from yoga it is not necessary to accomplish the perfect text book posture. It is the effects on the subtle energy system that are important, not the outward appearance.

Many teachers of Iyengar yoga use an assortment of props to help the correct alignment, which are particularly useful if you have a specific problem. When the body is aligned with the aid of various props, the energy is able to circulate in the correct way and begin the work of healing. Gradually, even the oldest most established patterns of disharmony will begin to change. Once the breath and the imagination is brought to work, the new patterns are introduced. Some teachers hold restorative classes in which the body may be supported in various ways to allow total relaxation in each position: the combination of opening and relaxing, while completely supported, gives the body a taste of the fully achieved asana.

During my slow recovery from pneumonia, my yoga teacher insisted that I spend most of the class lying over a wooden slatted bench. Very gradually my chest began to open up, loosen up, and I could breathe again without pain. The shape of the slatted wood acted as a gentle reminder to my spine of its intended position and function. In the same class an elderly woman avoided a hip replacement operation by performing simple forward bends while propped up on bolsters and cushions. When she first came to the class she was in constant pain, scared to attempt any movement at all. Within just a few weeks she had begun to relax and release and, with her body fully supported, she could begin to regain mobility in her joints.

With any accident, illness or injury the body tends to make adjustments to compensate. The pains in my chest caused my shoulders to round and my upper spine to collapse in an act of protection. At the time there was no question of doing anything different. Maybe in the short term this protective action is necessary, particularly in the case of a life-threatening situation, when something within the cellular consciousness seems to recognise its immortality. But these habits tend to stick. Fear within the body immobilises us and even when the protection is no longer needed, we find the pattern difficult to shake off. Sometimes the body needs reassurance that to stretch and release will not mean annihilation. When the joints become locked in rigidity we feel that if we move them we will break in two. We must always relax and release before we move and stretch.

So when you are working with the exercises that follow remember that the intention of hatha yoga is to perfect the energy system, not merely the physical body. We are working with subtle energy, with prana, and even if you are unable to make the physical movements, you can still use the consciousness and the breath, and the effect will be apparent.

Salutation to the Sun

The exercise sequence called surya namaskara, or salutation to the sun, is a beautifully choreographed series of movements which provides the necessary stretch for each part of the spine. It is not traditionally a part of yoga practice, but is often used before other asanas as a kind of warm-up exercise. As suggested by its name, it is often recommended first thing in the morning to loosen up all the joints of the body and to massage the internal organs, but it can be performed at any time of day to restore vitality.

The salutation to the sun consists of twelve movements

performed in a continual cycle. The movements are said to correspond to the twelve signs of the zodiac. Each movement is also linked with the energy centres and in advanced practice a mantra is also chanted.

I usually go through the sequence three times, once slowly with attention to the physical stretch and extension, a second time with attention to the breath, and co-ordinating each movement to the in- and out-breath, and a third time with concentration on the energy centres. It is helpful to become familiar with the physical movement before worrying too much about the breath and the concentration. They both come in time. If you are already familiar with the physical postures, focusing the attention on the chakras brings another dimension to the practice.

There are many variations to the practice of this sequence – the co-ordination of the breath and the concentration on the energy centres follow the instruction of Swami Satyananda Saraswati.

The Movements:

Stand with the feet together and the spine erect. Spend a few moments to check that you are straight and standing as tall as you can. Feel the weight evenly on the feet, the knees stretched, the hips level. Place the hands on the front hip bones and check that one is not higher than the other. Try to adjust.

Stretch the spine up from the pelvis, using the contact of the feet on the floor to give you lift, stretch up through the legs, the hips and the spine.

Relax the shoulders and the neck. Pull the chin slightly inwards towards the top of the chest, keeping the chest open. The collar bones should move upwards as the chin moves downwards, so that there is not a collapse in the upper chest.

Stand for a few moments in this stretched position, breathing deeply.

1   Bring the hands together at the level of the chest in the Indian form of greeting (Fig. 28).

2   Keeping the hands in the same position, move the fingers towards the centre of the chest, extend the wrists and inner arms, then extend the hands over the head, fully stretching the whole body and bending slightly backwards (Fig. 29).

3   After a full extension, relax down from the waist and allow the hands to fall towards the floor (Fig. 30).

4   Place the hands firmly on the floor, level with the toes, bending the knees if necessary, and step backwards with the right foot. Allow the knee to rest on the floor and look upwards. This action naturally curves the top of the spine gently backwards (Fig. 31).

5   Take the weight back on to the hands and move the left leg back to join the right. Push upwards with the hands and straighten the legs, creating a right-angle between the upper and lower limbs. This is often called the 'mountain position' (Fig. 32).

6   Slowly bring the weight of the upper body over the hands until the arms are perpendicular to the floor. Bend the elbows, and slowly lower the upper body to the floor as if preparing to do a press-up (Fig. 33).

7   Allow the lower body to contact the floor, the toes resting flat on the floor. Push up with the hands. Stretch the neck and raise the chin upwards, looking up and back. This is the 'cobra position' (Fig. 34).

Fig 28

Fig 29

Fig 30

Fig 31

Fig 32

Fig 33

8 Tuck the toes under, push up and back with the hands, bringing the body back into mountain pose. Stretch the legs and push upwards with the hands (Fig. 35).

9 Bring the right leg forward, allow the left knee to rest on the floor, and look up (Fig. 36).

10 With the weight on the hands, bring the left foot forward next to the right. Relax in the forward bending position (Fig. 37).

11 Slowly come up, and stretch the hands above the head, fully extending the whole body (Fig. 38).

12 Bring the hands together above the head and slowly return to bring them back to the salutation position in front of the heart (Fig. 39).

Repeat, leading with the left foot.

After you have repeated this series of exercises a few times, over a week or so, you will begin to find your own flow of movement. Its value is that it works on each part of the spine, extending and flexing. It exercises the hip joints and the shoulder joints, the wrists and the ankles. It also massages the internal organs, aiding digestion and elimination.

Breathing:

Once you are familiar with the physical movements, try co-ordinating the breath as follows:

1 Breathe calmly and deeply while in the first position. This posture brings a feeling of centred concentration.

Fig 34

Fig 35

Fig 36

Fig 37

Fig 38

Fig 39

2 Take a deep breath in as you stretch up.

3 Breathe out fully as you relax and stretch forward.

4 Move the right foot back and breathe in fully as you arch the back.

5 Breathe out as you push with the hands and stretch up into the mountain position.

6 Hold the breath at the exhalation as you move closer to the ground.

7 Breathe in deeply as you arch the spine backwards into the cobra position.

8 Breathe out as you move into the mountain position.

9 Breathe in as you bring the right foot forwards.

10 Breathe out as you bring the left foot forward and relax forwards.

11 Breathe in as you stretch the body up, arms stretched over the head.

12 Breathe out as you return to the starting position.

Breathe deeply and calmly before you begin the next round.

Concentration on the Chakras:

Once you are familiar with the physical movements and the breathing, a further stage incorporates concentration to the energy centres. In a later section we will look at exercises to become familiar with the position of the energy centres. You may like to try this practice first.

1 In the first position, concentrate on the heart centre. We saw that humility is the protector of the heart, and this hand position, or mudra, is associated with humility. It is used as a greeting throughout southern Asia, and is particularly used between student and teacher, disciple and guru as a mark of respect. As a greeting it recognises the divinity residing in all beings, and the interconnectedness of life.

2 As you stretch upwards and extend the chest and throat in the second position, concentrate to the throat centre. Stretch, release and relax all tension in the throat.

3 While bending forwards bring your attention to the second chakra in the lower abdomen. Contract the abdominal muscles as you exhale.

4 As you assume the fourth position, look directly forwards and upwards and bring your attention to the centre between the eyebrows.

5 Moving backwards into the mountain position, bring your awareness down to the throat centre. Here the back of the neck is stretched and the front contracted.

6 While holding the exhalation for the prone position, concentrate on the manipura or navel centre.

7 As you move forwards into the cobra position, bring the concentration down to the lower abdomen as you inhale. Feel rooted in the lower centre as you stretch upwards and forwards.

8 Concentrate on the throat centre as you move back into the mountain position, exhaling deeply.

9 Bend the right leg and bring it forward, concentrating to the brow centre as you look up and inhale.

10 Exhale deeply concentrating on the lower abdomen as you bring the left leg beside the right and relax forward.

11 Inhale as you stretch upwards, concentrating to the throat chakra.

12 Exhale and bring the hands back to the position of salutation, focusing on the heart centre.

Effects:

This exercise acts as an all-round tone-up. It keeps the physical body supple, the energy body supple, the energy centres activated. It is quite similar to the basic qi gong sequence in that it can be done in many ways with differing effects. It is possible to do the movements very slowly, holding each posture while breathing naturally. The sequence can be performed very quickly, providing a more aerobic exercise. Co-ordinating the breath with the movements adds a further dimension, as the qi or prana begins to have a more obvious effect. Performed slowly with the breath focused and the concentration turned within to the energy centres, it becomes a kind of moving concentration/meditation.

Simplified Spinal Stretches:

If you have difficulty with this exercise, the more gentle general warm-up sequences in my previous book, *Reclaiming the Wisdom of the Body*, will be more suitable. This is a general movement, for those who are reasonably flexible, and not intended to treat any specific imbalances. If you require information on ways to deal with specific physical problems and imbalances, *Reclaiming the Wisdom of the Body* attempts to provide guidance of that kind.

If your joints are not flexible, you can give the spine the stretch that it requires by using a support of some kind. A window sill, a chair or bannister rail, for example, may be useful. Figures 40–42 show various ways of using a support to obtain the required stretch. And remember, even if you cannot physically move into the full position, you can use the breath and the imagination to energise the subtle channels.

Sideways stretches and spinal twists:

Our spines have developed to give us a complex range of movements. They are capable not only of extension and flexion but also sideways stretching and rotation. The practice of sideways stretches and spinal twists will therefore keep the spine moving freely in all directions. The amount of movement possible differs quite naturally with each individual. Never stretch too much. Co-ordinate each extension of movement with an exhalation, which makes it difficult to carry tension. Injury comes from resistance, and resistance from tension. Learning to relax and release as you extend is the most beneficial way to get the maximum effect from exercise.

The following five simple stretches give a range of possible movements:

1 Stand erect with the feet parallel and slightly apart. Check that the spine is straight and extend upwards. The hands should rest naturally at the sides. Breathe in, and with an exhalation allow the right hand to move down the right leg,

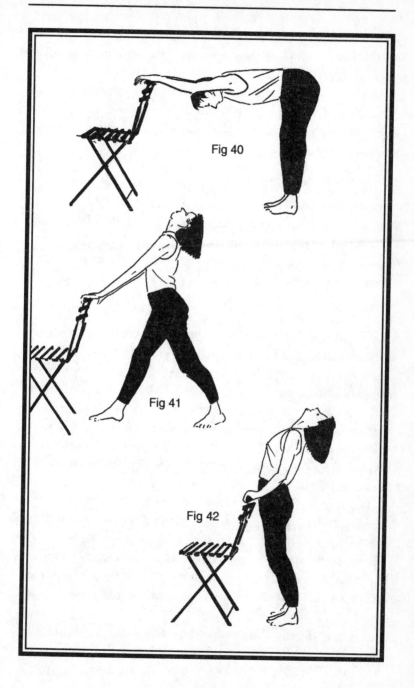

Fig 40

Fig 41

Fig 42

slowly bending the body to the side. Make sure that the trunk does not move forwards or backwards, but remains in the same vertical plane (Fig. 43).

Return to the upright position with the inhalation. Exhale and repeat the movement to the left. Repeat five times, using the breath and keeping the awareness focused on the spine.

2 With the feet wider apart, but still parallel, stretch up. Inhale, and with the exhalation rotate the body round to the left, looking towards the right foot behind you, and pointing towards the right foot with the left hand (Fig. 44).

Return to the centre as you inhale. Exhale as you repeat the movement to the right, looking and pointing towards the left foot. Repeat five times.

3 Sit on the floor with the spine straight and legs stretched straight out in front of you. Bring up the right knee and place the right foot flat on the floor beside the left knee. Extend the spine upwards, and then with an exhalation, twist round to the left keeping the upward extension. Place the right elbow inside the right knee and use it to lever you round. Place the left hand on the floor behind you. Breathe evenly while maintaining the position for a few minutes. Return to the centre and then repeat to the other side (Fig. 45).

For a greater stretch, follow the first instructions, as above, but first twist to the right, so that you are twisting towards the side of the raised knee rather than away from it. Bring the left elbow to the outside of the right knee, and twist, looking over the right shoulder. It is important to lift up sufficiently in from the pelvis to allow the twist to begin in the lumbar vertebrae.

4 Lie flat on the floor with the arms outstretched to the sides. Bring up the knees and place the feet flat on the floor

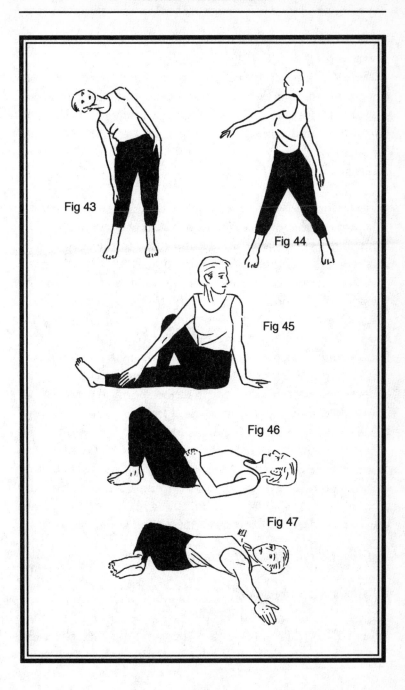

Fig 43

Fig 44

Fig 45

Fig 46

Fig 47

in front of the buttocks. Allow the spine to relax and release towards the floor (Fig. 46).

Inhale deeply and with an exhalation allow the knees to drop towards the floor. If your knees go to the left, look towards your right hand, keeping the shoulders on the floor. Breathe naturally and with each out-breath relax and release further. Inhale as you bring the knees back to the centre. Repeat to the other side (Fig. 47).

When working with these simple spinal exercises, remember that each of the internal organs has a nerve attachment to the spine. These nerve attachments also relate to the acupuncture points used to stimulate organ function. If we keep the spine healthy, which means maintaining a good blood supply to the nerves and a good energy supply to the meridians, many organic imbalances will be cured. Dr Motoyama's device for diagnosing the acupuncture meridians (AMI) is able to give an accurate picture of spinal abnormalities merely by measuring the energy of the acupuncture meridians at the fingers and toes. It will also prescribe specific yoga exercises to work with that particular area of imbalance.

We have seen that the spine is more than the centre of the nervous system. The subtle energy channels which flow within the spine are the centre of the subtle energy system. The three main nadi, the ida, pingala and sushumna, flow within the central spinal channel, and breathing exercises have been devised to clear and harmonise these three channels.

Purification of the Subtle Energy Channels

Alternate Nostril Breathing

One of the basic breathing exercises used in yoga practice aims to create balance within the right and left channels, the ida and pingala nadi. We have seen that these two nadis are contained within the spinal cord, beginning at the first chakra at the base of the spine and ending in the right and left nostrils respectively. Breathing through alternate nostrils is one of the traditional practices to purify the subtle energy system and to balance to ida and pingala nadi. This could also be said to create balance between yin and yang, fire and water, the sympathetic and parasympathetic nervous system.

Traditionally pranayama exercises are carried out after asana, or physical exercise, and before meditation and concentration.

Method:

Sit in one of the suggested meditation positions (Figs. 23, 24, 25). As with the circulation of light, it is of greatest importance that the spine is straight, so try each of the positions and find one that gives the most comfort and stability. Concentration is important and you do not want to be distracted by discomfort. Sitting with the legs folded in front of you is the preferred position, and if you use as many cushions or supports as you need to enable your knees to reach the floor, you can reduce them in time. You need to be stable, and you need to have a straight spine. Sitting on a chair with your feet firmly on the floor is often the best option if your hips are inflexible.

Once you have found your preferred position, place the hands on the knees, palms facing downwards. Imagine a thread from the top of the head is gently pulling the spine erect, push down with your feet or legs to make a solid contact with the floor. Try to retain this feeling of stability and inner space.

Stage One:

Take the right hand to the face and place the first and second fingers between the eyebrows. Allow the thumb to rest gently at the right side of the nose, the third finger at the left. Breathe deeply and calmly for a few breaths.

1 Place the thumb over the right nostril to block the air. Inhale and exhale through the left nostril for five inhalations, five exhalations. Allow the breathing to be natural and as silent as possible. Be aware of the air gently moving through the left nostril.

2 Release the thumb and close the left nostril with the third finger. Inhale and exhale through the right nostril for five inhalations, five exhalations.

This is one round. Five rounds takes about ten minutes, if your breathing is fairly deep and even, and this would be sufficient as a preparation for further exercises. Counting the breath also aids concentration. This practice should be carried out every day for two weeks before moving on to the next stage.

Stage Two:

Prepare in the same way, with the fingers in the same positions as for stage one.

1 Place the thumb over the right nostril, and breathe in through the left. Once the inhalation is complete, close the nostril with the third finger.

2 Release the thumb, and exhale through the right nostril. Inhale through the same nostril and then close once again with the thumb.

3 Release the third finger and exhale through the left nostril. This makes one complete cycle. Continue by breathing in again through the left.

Once you are familiar with the rhythm of the exercise – it is very simple to do, more difficult to explain – begin to count the length of the inhalation and the length of the exhalation. If you breathe in to a count of three, breathe out to a count of three, if you breathe in to a count of four, breathe out to a count of four. Just do what is comfortable. There should be no sense of strain. Remember that you change fingers after the inhalation, exhaling, then inhaling to the same side. After a few days try increasing the count by one, but always keep the inhalation and the exhalation the same. If there is any discomfort, stop the practice and go back to a lower count. The idea is to balance the breath within the left and the right nostrils and to balance the inhalation with the exhalation.

Once this method has been practised for a few weeks, try stage three.

Stage Three:

1   Using the same method described above, inhale through the left nostril. Close both nostrils and retain the breath for a count of three. Exhale through the right nostril.

2   Inhale through the right nostril, close both nostrils and retain the breath for a count of three. Exhale through the left nostril.

It is not advisable to extend the length of breath retention, or to retain the exhalation unless you are practising with a qualified teacher. The above practice is sufficient to clear the subtle channels from blockages, to regulate and balance the flow of prana in the ida and pingala nadis. Regular practice will calm the mind, bring stability to the emotions, help to cleanse toxins from the blood. By increasing the supply of oxygen it will aid the production of energy through cellular metabolism, and also increase the supply of oxygen to the brain.

If at any time during practice you feel dizzy, stop immediately and sit quietly, breathing naturally.

Preparation for Concentration

Before moving on to practices which require concentration and visualisation, try this simple exercise to stabilise the body. When practising alternate nostril breathing we are working with the prana, and the effects are simply from the repetition of the breath. If you occasionally move the body or adjust your position it will not have a detrimental effect. But when working with mental concentration and visualisation, it is helpful to develop the ability to sit very still. Movement of the body will create a movement within the mind and detract from the concentration. A comfortable and stable sitting position becomes increasingly important as you aim to develop inner concentration.

Method:

1 Sit with the spine erect, the chin tucked slightly in. Breathe deeply and evenly. Count five with the inhalation, five with the exhalation. Continue counting with the breath until you feel relaxed and still. Feel aware of the legs or the feet pressing down into the floor. Imagine that they are roots, like the roots of a tree keeping you stable. From these roots you are able to grow upwards with strength and stability.

2 Become aware of your body and note any sensations. Scan through the body and be aware of any feelings of heat and cold, tension and stiffness. If there is any pain, any itching, any discomfort, be aware of it but try not to react to it.

3 Focus on your head, and be aware of any sensations

within your head. Focus on your neck and be aware of any sensations within your neck. Focus on your chest and be aware of any sensations within your chest. In this way move slowly through the body focusing on each area in turn, remaining aware of any sensations you may feel. When you have completed at the feet, visualise the whole body and continue to be aware of any sensations in the body.

4 Remaining aware of the body feel the immobility of the body, feel that you are completely still, unable to move. No movement, no discomfort, only stillness.

5 Retaining the sense of stillness, bring your awareness back to the breath. Be aware of your breath without attempting to alter it in any way. Observe the breath as it flows in and out of the body, like the movement of waves on the shore. Remain aware of the body, holding the body and breath together in your mind. The body is completely still, the breath becomes more and more silent, until you are hardly breathing at all. There is no effort.

6 Maintain this sense of stillness and concentration. The body is still, the breath is silent, the mind is quiet.

7 As you bring the exercise to an end, slowly regain awareness of the body, feeling your relationship to the floor and the space around you. Be aware of the hands resting on the knees. Breathe more deeply.

Developing Awareness of the Chakras

Before we move on to the exercises which involve concentration on the subtle energy channels, let us take some time to familiarise ourselves with the locations of the chakras. Most of the internal exercises of yoga involve looking within

187

the body and directing the concentration and the prana or subtle energy to that area. The breath is used in order to aid concentration, to focus the mind and to direct the prana. Some people can do this very easily, others need practice. Some people see all kinds of things, others see nothing. It does not really matter. The important thing is the concentration and the practice.

When we focus the mind within, it is important not to strain in any way. The area between and behind the eyebrows should remain relaxed and open. The mind should be calm, there should be no forcing. Always be gentle. Do not force the breath. Do not hold the breath. With each inhalation there may be a slight contraction, with each exhalation a complete relaxation. Any force or strain or attempt to lengthen the breath unnaturally will only result in a headache.

Sit comfortably with the spine straight. The body posture is intended to help your concentration, so try to be comfortable and relaxed. Close the eyes, and move the awareness through the body, releasing any tension. Try to feel that the right and left sides of the body are quite even. Adjust your posture if it helps you to feel balanced and stable.

With the exception of the base chakra, each of the chakras has a root connected to the spinal column and a trigger point on the front of the body. As we slowly progress through the body, we will attempt to locate each of these centres in turn. We will begin with the trigger point and then move directly back to the point on the spine. Some centres may be more easy to imagine than others. Again, just gently bring consciousness to the area and be aware. We are not trying to achieve anything, only awareness. The chakras are often likened to flowers, and their functioning similar to the opening and closing of the petals of a flower. It is not possible to force open the petals of a flower, they open naturally when gently brought in contact with the light of the sun. Similarly the chakras respond when they are gently brought into contact with the light of consciousness (Fig. 48).

1 Sit comfortably, with the spine straight, the chin slightly tucked in. If you are able to sit with the feet folded in front of you, try to exert pressure with the lower heel to the perineum. The base chakra does not have a trigger point, but exists at this one point within the perineum. Direct your attention to the perineum. Feel the pressure of your heel. Feel as if you are breathing in and out through this area. Try to be aware of a pulsation as you breathe in and out through this point. Be aware that this is your root, the centre of your survival instincts, your feelings of security within the physical world, your contact with the earth.

2 Bring the attention to the pubic bone. If possible, allow the upper heel to exert pressure at the top of the pubic bone in the midline of the lower abdomen. As you check your posture and adjust your spine upwards, you will feel a natural tension at this point as you lengthen the lower back. Try to retain that feeling, be aware of that point. This is the centre of your sexuality, of your unconscious; your ability to pro-create. Its element is water. Breathe gently as if you are breathing in and out of this point.

Once you have established the breath, breathe in and with the breath move the awareness straight back to the lower spine, to the junction of the sacrum and the coccyx; exhale as you bring the attention back to the pubic bone. Continue breathing gently and moving the awareness backwards and forwards, allow the breath to create a link between the point at the front of the body and the point at the back.

189

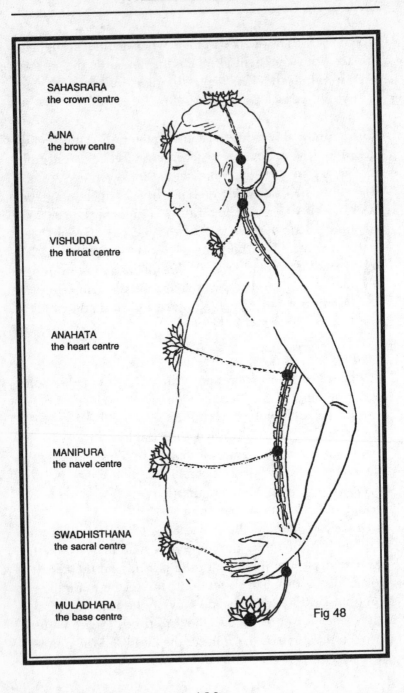

SAHASRARA
the crown centre

AJNA
the brow centre

VISHUDDA
the throat centre

ANAHATA
the heart centre

MANIPURA
the navel centre

SWADHISTHANA
the sacral centre

MULADHARA
the base centre

Fig 48

3 Move the awareness up to the navel, checking that the spine is still straight, adjust your position if necessary to remain comfortable. Be aware of the navel. Imagine that the breath is moving in and out through the navel. Be aware of any movement or pulsation in the area.

When the breath is steady and the focus established, inhale and move the consciousness with the breath straight back to a point on the spine, exhale as your consciousness returns to the navel. Continue breathing in a relaxed and regular way, breathing in through the navel and back to the spine, breathing out as you move your awareness forwards towards the navel. Imagine that the breath is creating a passage between the navel and the point on the spine, the root of the manipura chakra. This is the centre of the fire element, of digestion and assimilation.

4 Move the awareness to the sternum. Feel as if you are breathing in and out from the centre of the chest at the level of the heart. Be aware of this area of the body, be aware of your heart beat. Feel the breath and the rhythm of the heart. Inhale as you move the awareness back to a point on the spine at the level of the heart. Be aware of this point. Relax and release any tension. Breathe out as you move the awareness forwards to the sternum. Imagine that the breath is creating a channel between the points on the front and the back of the body.

5 Move the awareness to the throat. Imagine that you are breathing in and out through the base of the throat. Keep the neck extended and the chin slightly tucked in. As you tuck the chin in be aware of the slight contraction at the base of the throat. Focus your attention and your breath to this point. Breathe evenly in and out through this point. Move the breath and the awareness to the back of the neck as you

inhale, to the base of the throat as you exhale. Feel that the breath fills this area of the throat from front to back.

6 Bring the awareness to the space between the eyebrows. Relax and release any tension. Imagine that you are breathing in and out through the brow centre, the meeting point of the three subtle channels, the ida, the pingala and the sushumna nadis. Focus all your attention to this point, but remain relaxed and do not strain either physically or mentally. When you are comfortable and centred at the brow centre, move the awareness back to the point deep within the brain which is the site of the pineal gland, the root of the ajna chakra. Breathe in as you move your focus backwards, allow the breath to fill the brain. Exhale as you focus once again between the eyebrows. Gradually try to focus more and more precisely on the point of the ajna chakra deep within the brain. This is quite difficult as we have no point of reference, but just keep breathing gently, and be aware of any sensations.

As you breathe in the head seems to expand with light and energy, as you exhale the head seems to contract.

7 Let go of the concentration, but keep the rhythm of the breath. Visualise the whole body filled with energy and filled with light. Try to hold the awareness of all the energy centres – their trigger points at the front of the body, their roots at the back. Breathe deeply and evenly for a few minutes before slowly coming back to the awareness of the physical body sitting on the floor. Be aware of your surroundings, of any noises that you can hear. Slowly open your eyes. Stretch your fingers and toes, arms and legs, and slowly come out of the sitting position.

If at any time you feel dizzy or nauseous stop the concentration and breathe naturally. Be aware of the whole body, the legs resting on the floor, the arms resting on the legs. Slowly move your fingers and toes and open your eyes. Lie flat on the floor for a few minutes. If it helps, bring your knees up to your abdomen. Over-concentration on one centre can occasionally bring up strange feelings within the body or the mind. At the beginning don't spend too long on any one centre. The exercises above are intended to familiarise us with the energy centres. Concentrating on one centre for a prolonged period of time is not recommended until you have become quite used to the exercises and are sure that you have no ill effects.

The exercises that follow are recommended for purifying the subtle channels and balancing the energy centres, and are traditionally a prerequisite for any depth work with the chakras.

Purification of the Subtle Energy Channels

Within yoga tradition dating back to the Vedas and Upanishads, there are many practices which involve focusing the attention on the channels of subtle energy, both within the spine and at the front of the body. We will learn three simple techniques: one which works with the front channel, one with the back channel and one which combines both. They are very similar to the practice of turning the light around in the Chinese tradition, though each uses its own imagery. The subtle energy channels can be visualised as thin, luminous, transparent tubes; the sushumna nadi within the spinal channel is visualised as a silver thread which lies within the tube. The breath is like a wind travelling through the tube, the prana within the breath a sparkling stream of energy. Once you are able to visualise the channel, try to imagine the inside of the channel. Move through the channel with the breath. The spinal channels pass through the roots of the chakra, the front channel passes through the trigger points or flowers. As the breath moves through the channels it acts as a broom, sweeping away debris; or a wind blowing away dust (Fig. 49).

Method:

Sit comfortably with the spine erect. If possible sit on a pad with the feet drawn up. Place the heel of the foot against the perineum, exerting a slight pressure to the lower energy centre, the root chakra.

Place the hands on the knees with the palms facing upwards. This movement of the hands and arms opens the chest and brings the shoulders back. Pull the head slightly backwards and tuck in the chin. Bring the first finger into contact with the thumb, creating a circle. This simple mudra (hand movement) brings together the meridians of the lung and large intestine, the first and second meridians of acupuncture, aiding energy flow, and symbolising a turning of energy within.

Breathe deeply, and feel the stillness of the body. Try to feel steady and immobile as you prepare to focus your attention within.

1 Bring the awareness to the muladhara chakra, the root chakra at the perineum. As you inhale, slightly contract the muscles in the perineum, as you exhale, release.

2 When the body feels still and calm, the breath rhythmical and relaxed, inhale and bring the awareness to the lower abdomen, just above the pubic bone, exhale as you allow your attention to fall back to the perineum.

3 With the next inhalation bring the breath and the concentration straight up to the navel; with the exhalation, allow the concentration to drop back to the perineum.

4 With the next inhalation, bring the breath and the attention to the sternum, with the exhalation bring it back to the perineum.

5 With the next inhalation, bring the breath and the concentration to the throat; with the exhalation bring it back down to the perineum.

6 With the next inhalation, bring the breath and the attention to the space between the eyebrows; with the exhalation, bring it back to the perineum.

7 Continue to breathe between the base chakra and the brow centre. Raising the awareness to the brow centre with each in-breath, returning to the base with each exhalation. Be aware of each centre as you move up and down the body with the breath. Keep the slight contraction of the perineal muscles with each inhalation, relax with each exhalation.

Visualisation:

8 While continuing the movement of the breath, try to visualise the breath moving through a luminous, transparent tube which stretches from the base chakra to the space between the eyebrows. Visualise the inside of the tube, with the breath and the consciousness moving within the tube.

9 Visualise the prana within the breath as a stream of sparkling energy. The prana creates the movement, the prana creates the channel. As you concentrate on the bright stream of energy, allow the breath to become quiet. Just be aware of the channel and of the prana.

As you prepare to end the meditation, bring your awareness back to the breath, and back to the body. Be aware of your physical body, your contact with the floor, the pressure of your hands on your knees. Take two or three deep breaths before you open your eyes. Slowly move the fingers and toes, the hands and the feet.

Stretch the limbs and rotate the joints before you attempt to get up.

Once you have practised the exercise a few times, and feel confident about the location of the chakras, it is not always necessary to perform the first few stages. It is however a good exercise to bring your awareness to each centre in turn and assess how you feel. Be aware which centres seem easy to access, easy to imagine, and which are hard to find. Be aware of any pain and discomfort. Use this as a simple exercise to become familiar with the energy centres. It is not necessary to do anything. Just breathe naturally, and bring your awareness to the area.

Concentration on the Sushumna

The sushumna is the primary nadi, flowing within the spinal cord from the base chakra and touching the root of each of the chakras in turn until it reaches the root of the brow centre, deep within the brain. This exercise involves the visualisation of the breath moving from the base chakra to the root of the ajna chakra, which is located at the pineal gland. Though the function of this gland is little understood in Western biological science, in the Indian tradition it is the bridge between the physical and subtle dimensions. As the ajna chakra is the centre of command, it is also said to control the other centres (Fig. 50).

Method:

Adopt a comfortable sitting position, as above. Breathe deeply, feeling the body rooted to the floor, the spine extended.

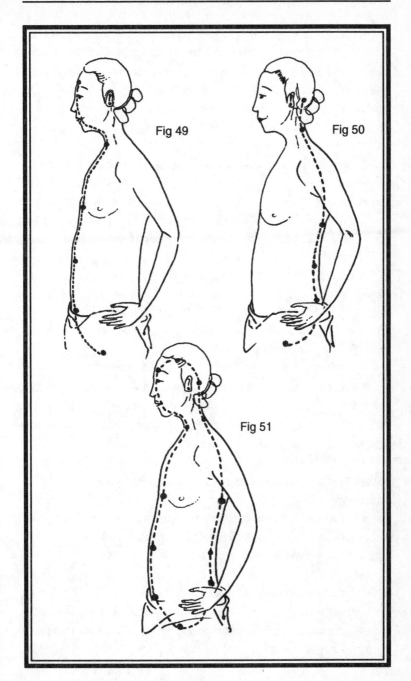

Fig 49

Fig 50

Fig 51

1   Bring the awareness to the root chakra at the perineum. As you inhale, slightly contract the muscles in the perineum, as you exhale, release. The root chakra is not differentiated into root and flower, it is just one point. So this stage of the practice is the same as in the previous exercise. Breathe gently concentrating on this centre.

2   When the body feels still and calm, the breath rhythmical and relaxed, inhale and bring the awareness to the base of the spine, to the point where the coccyx meets the sacrum. This is the root of the swadhisthana chakra. Exhale as you allow the concentration to fall back to the perineum.

3   With the next inhalation bring the breath and the awareness through the spinal column to the point directly behind the navel; with the exhalation, allow the concentration to drop back to the perineum. This is the root of the manipura chakra.

4   With the next inhalation, bring the breath and the awareness to the point on the spine behind the sternum, with the exhalation bring it back to the perineum. This is the root of the heart centre, the anahata chakra.

5   With the next inhalation, bring the breath and the concentration through the spine to the back of the neck where the cervical and thoracic vertebrae meet; with the exhalation bring it back down to the perineum. This is the root of the throat centre, the vishuddha chakra.

6   With the next inhalation, bring the breath and the concentration through the spinal column, through the neck and into the brain; with the exhalation, bring it back to the perineum. This is the root of the brow centre, the ajna chakra.

7 Continue to breathe between the base chakra and the root of the ajna chakra deep within the brain. Raise the awareness with each in-breath, and return to the base with each exhalation. Be aware of the root of each chakra as you move up and down the spine with the breath. Keep the slight contraction to the perineal muscles with each inhalation, relax with each exhalation.

Visualisation:

8 Try to visualise the breath moving through a luminous, transparent tube which stretches from the base chakra through the spine and into the centre of the brain. Visualise the inside of the tube, with the breath and the consciousness moving within the tube.

9 Visualise the prana within the breath as a stream of sparkling energy moving through the transparent tube within the spinal column. The prana creates the movement, the prana creates the channel. Be aware of the channel and of the prana, the breath and the consciousness travelling through the channel.

10 Once you become familiar and comfortable with the exercise, and are able to visualise the channel quite steadily, try to imagine the chakras along the channel. Bring your awareness to the perineum, and visualise the root chakra as a point of bright light; then bring your awareness to the base of the spine and visualise the root of the swadhisthana chakra as a point of bright light. Move the awareness up to the point behind the navel and imagine the root of the manipura chakra as a point of bright light. Move on to the point behind the sternum and visualise the root of the heart chakra as a point of bright light. Bring the awareness to the back of the neck and visualise the root of the throat chakra as a point

of bright light. Move the awareness up the spinal channel to deep within the brain and visualise the root of the brow centre as a point of bright light.

11 Bring your attention back to the breath, moving the awareness up the spinal channel with the inhalation, down the spinal channel with the exhalation. Imagine the breath and the prana entering and moving through each of the chakras on its way. Keep the breath and the movement of the awareness focused and steady, with no strain and no holding of the breath. The breath should be slow and steady and natural. Do not force the concentration. If the visualisation is not there, just continue the movement of the breath, but be light and relaxed.

As you prepare to end the concentration, bring your awareness back to the physical body. Be aware of your contact with the floor, the pressure of your hands on your knees. Take two or three deep breaths before you open your eyes. Slowly move the fingers and toes, the hands and the feet. Stretch the limbs and rotate the joints before you attempt to get up.

Circulation Through the Subtle Channels

Here we will look at the method for circulating energy through the subtle channels according to Satyananda Saraswati. The yoga exercises that I learned with Dr Motoyama were based on the teaching and tradition of Swami Satyananda Saraswati. He considered Satyananda's teachings to be closest to the traditional and also to his own experiences of awakening the chakras. Satyananda Saraswati teaches a circulation through the subtle channels which is similar to the circulation of light in Chinese yoga practice. But whereas the circulation of light generally begins at the root chakra, follows the spinal channel to the brow centre with the inhalation, and then down the mid-front channel with the exhalation, Satyananda's exercise begins at the root chakra and moves up the frontal channel with the inhalation and down the spinal channel with the exhalation. There is, however, an indication that the practice may be reversed. Dr Motoyama explains that the direction of the practice is flexible, the importance being to keep the energy moving and the channel open. Research during the past few years at Dr Motoyama's Human Science Institute in Tokyo has suggested that there is a tendency for subtle energy to flow up the frontal channel and down the back channel in women, and up the back channel and down the front in men. But this is not a rule. Energy can flow in either direction, and the slightest fluctuation in circumstance was able to affect the outcome of the research.

Dr Motoyama did not consider his research to be conclusive, and currently advises his students to try both methods and to see which is most comfortable. The system of numbering acupuncture points along the subtle energy channels, which is a recent innovation, has galvanised the concept that energy moves in a particular direction. But it is always important to remember that this is only a tendency. Information can always move in either direction. You could say that it is the movement of information that creates the energy channels, which is of course what makes this kind of energy work such a dynamic tool for transformation.

According to traditional Chinese theory, the direction of the flow will tend to create a more yin or yang effect. Bringing energy through the spinal channel from the base to the crown brings yang energy into the brain; it is stimulating and awakening. In the Indian tradition this would be related to raising of kundalini which resides in the base chakra and must ultimately find its home deep within the brain. Conversely focusing on the movement up the front channel may be seen to have a more yin effect, bringing nourishment and stillness to the inner organs, the heart and mind. But this is an oversimplification of an ancient practice which aims to balance and purify, stimulate and calm.

Try for yourself, and find which practice you prefer. It could be that at times one practice is more beneficial – but it is good to be adaptable. Learn to look within and trust your own feelings.

This is a simplification of Satyananda's exercise. It follows the first stages but there are more which also include the repetition of mantras (Fig. 51).

Method:

1 Sit comfortably with the spine erect. Rest the hands on the knees with palms facing upwards. Tuck the chin in slightly.

Stage One:

2 Bring the awareness to the root chakra at the perineum. As you inhale, slightly contract the muscles in the perineum, as you exhale, release. Breathe gently concentrating on this centre for a few minutes. Feel the body to be rooted and still.

3 When the body feels still and calm, the breath rhythmical and relaxed, bring the awareness through the frontal channel to the second chakra trigger point at the pubic bone. Breathe naturally at this stage. Continue up to the navel, the heart, the throat, the brow, imagining the chakras as points of light.

4 After reaching the brow centre, move backwards to the ajna chakra deep within the brain. Allow your awareness to move down through the spinal channel through the roots of the chakras to the base of the spine.

5 Immediately begin another circuit, still breathing gently and naturally. Imagine the pathway of the subtle channels with the chakras and their trigger points as points of light. Continue until the visualisation feels natural and steady.

Stage Two:

6 Roll back the tongue so that the bottom of the tongue rests gently on the roof of the mouth. Exhale deeply.

7 As you inhale, move the awareness up the front energy channel to the brow centre.

8 Exhale as you move down the spinal channel to the base.

9 Immediately begin the next round, and following the inhalation and the exhalation, imagining the energy centres as bright lights strung along an elliptical pathway of energy. Be aware of the breath moving within the channel. Be aware of the prana moving within the breath. You may visualise the prana as a bright current of sparkling light. Keep your concentration with the movement and with the breath.

As you bring your consciousness back to the body, the space you are sitting in, listen to any sounds around you. Take a few deep breaths. Feel your weight on the floor. Gradually move your fingers and toes, then your hands and feet.

This kind of concentration and circulation of the breath through the subtle energy channels forms the basis for much meditation practice. It is a kind of preparation that within the Indian yoga tradition is seen as indispensable for progress. In Japan before we sat in the shrine room each morning, we would sweep and dust. It was a preparation of the space for meditation, but also symbolic of the preparation of ourselves for meditation. This kind of pranayama, with concentration to the psychic channels acts in a similar way, cleaning and purifying the inner space. If more advanced yoga techniques are attempted before this basic cleaning is performed there may be problems; imbalances within the subtle energy may manifest as physical illness or even as mental illness.

In the 1960s and '70s when young people in the West began experimenting with yoga there were many casualties. Often the mixture of so-called spiritual experience and drugs lead to experiences which were totally ungrounded. Within both the Indian and the Chinese tradition, the circulation of light/energy through the subtle channels is seen as the safest way to progress. Unless the subtle channels are clear and strong, any more advanced practices would at best be ineffective, at worst dangerous.

We have looked at both Chinese and Indian ideas of energy transformation, and at some of the techniques that are traditionally used to enhance these natural processes. Although there are some obvious similarities, in comparing the two systems we must be careful not to jump to conclusions, not to make analogies where there may be none. What is most obvious is that both the ancient Chinese and ancient Indian systems of yoga and health found that the two primary pathways of subtle energy at the back and the front of the body were the basis of all practice. Their understanding of the subtle energy centres has many similarities but also some differences – it does not mean that one is right and the other wrong, but that they are looking at slightly different things.

The Chinese understanding of subtle energy, as described in the first section of the book, is based on the Chinese classical texts of the third century BC. Qi gong exercises were in existence around this time and described in some detail. The yoga sutras of Patangali were written down at a similar time in history. Many of the teachings of

Daoist yoga and alchemy, however, date from the fourth to eighth centuries AD, and are very likely to contain the influence of Indian teachings. By the eighth century, practices such as the circulation of light may very well have been modified by Indian ideas. We know that Bodhidharma arrived in China at the beginning of the sixth century and introduced various forms of meditation and martial arts from southern India.

The purpose of the practice may have differed between the two cultures. The Chinese always professed to be interested in promoting health and longevity. The Daoist alchemists were searching for a way to transform the body – their hope to gain immortality. In the long history of Indian yoga, the aim of practice was often to escape the physical and return to a world of pure spirit. And although the Indian culture had a mature understanding of the energy/matter continuum, matter was often seen as an impediment to spirit, to such an extent that some saddhus to this day mutilate the body to show their contempt of and mastery over the material world. A split between mind and matter occurred in Hinduism, much as it occurred in the West, but whereas in the West the emphasis was on the material, in Hindu philosophy the emphasis was on mind and spirit.

Some schools of Hindu philosophy translate the concept of maya to mean that the physical world is an illusion, that the only reality is that of mind and spirit. The physical world must therefore be treated with contempt, as it is in opposition to spirit. According to Indian philosophy, the cycle of creation involves the descent of spirit into matter, and yoga is often seen as the tool to release spirit back to its origin. Twentieth-century teachers such as Sri Aurobindo have reintroduced the idea that it is our concept of reality that is the illusion. Maya is the subjective consciousness that perceives ourselves as separate. It is our failure to recognise the divine consciousness within ourselves and the subtle dimensions which are both behind and all around the material world which is the illusion. The descent of spirit into matter is continual, and the aim of the descent is the transformation of matter. The aim of the yoga of Sri Aurobindo is therefore a continual evolution of consciousness within an increasingly responsive and receptive body. Throughout history many schools of tantrism have kept these ideas alive, often in opposition to the Hindu orthodoxy.

Despising matter and despising the body has deeply affected our natural processes and our natural evolution. The resulting split in mind and body has had devastating effects on our mental, emotional and physical health. The Far Eastern traditions seem to have escaped this delusion, and it is here that much of their value lies.

The exercises given here are suggestions for practice as you feel your way back towards wholeness. The only way that we can monitor our success is to trust our own body wisdom. Trust yourself to know how you feel. If you have any doubts, trust that this is not for you and try something else. Accept that at times you need to move and stretch, at other times you need to sit and focus within. Learn to know what you need. The age of unquestioning acceptance of the guru seems to be coming to an end as we all aim towards self-responsibility. Teachings that have remained secret for many generations are being made more available. The most important thing is that we treat them with respect. So, to conclude, let us look at various ways to determine a practice which may be beneficial for each individual, beneficial for individual progress and discovery of the true nature. Let us look at the ways that both the Chinese and Indian traditions have addressed the physical, emotional and mental levels of our being, by working with the three cinnabar fields and the three obstructions.

STRENGTHENING THE GATE OF DESTINY

Although the energy centres of the lower abdomen are concerned with our more physical nature, their energy also exists in the more subtle realms. But it is the emotions that concern our physical well-being, our survival, our ability to procreate which tend to manifest there. When thinking about the lower cinnabar field, the hara, let us recap a little on the way each tradition sees this area of the lower abdomen.

In Chinese medicine it is the area of the water element; the gate of destiny being the fire within the water. The movement of the water element is downwards and its associated emotion is fear. It represents our roots and our stability but also our inherited energies and our ability to procreate. It governs the kidneys and the sexual organs, and is linked to the spine and the brain. Deep within the belly is the root of the energetic system of meridians, reflecting the origin of development in foetal life. On the front midline below the navel is the lower sea of qi.

In Chinese alchemy the two primary channels diverge at the base of the trunk, the water wheel reverses the natural inclination for the movement downwards, directing energy up through the spinal channel towards the cauldron of the gate of destiny where the dynamic balance of fire and water create the first possibility of transformation and transmutation. In front of the gate of destiny, the ox ploughs the field, symbolising that the constant repetition of exercise and awareness of the breath can prepare the field of consciousness for the mutation from base metal to gold.

In Japan the hara is the focus of attention in all martial art practices and in the sitting meditation of Zen. It is illustrated by the Bodhidharma figures which have their centre of gravity in the base, and however many times you try to knock them over they always return to stability. When we are centred in the lower abdomen there is stillness within the body, which is the prerequisite for stillness within the mind.

In the Indian system, the lower chakra, the muladhara, is our root and our foundation. It is the centre of our animal instinct, controlling the instinctual functions of eating and sleeping. It is our basic push for survival in the physical world. Instability in this area may manifest as a deep insecurity, possibly creating greed and anger. Stability will provide a good basis for growth. The subtle energy channels, the ida, pingala and sushumna, have their origin in the muladhara chakra, connecting the lowest centre to the spinal cord and the brain. This centre is ruled by the earth element within the Indian system. The natural movement of the prana in the lower abdomen is downward.

The second chakra, the swadhisthana, is the centre of sexuality and the growing awareness of the self. It controls individuation and sexual development. It is ruled by the water element and controls the unconscious. Imbalance of the swadhisthana chakra may manifest in emotional instability and sexual insecurity. There may be envy and jealousy and the need to possess the other in a relationship.

Untying the knot of Brahma, which is located within the lower abdomen, represents a freedom from the material world. If we are secure, we no longer feel attachment to possessions; if we are secure there is no longer a need to possess or be possessed by another.

When we work with exercises to strengthen this centre within the lower abdomen, we are working with the basis of our physical life. We are creating roots and stability which will allow us to move forward. While remaining constantly in touch with our source, we will create the required base for our future development.

The lower abdomen, or hara, is treated with the greatest

respect in the Far East. If the fire in the lower abdomen is diminished, there is a severe decline in usable energy, which may manifest as ME or other forms of energy depletion. Exercises are regularly performed to strengthen the hara and the energy of the lower abdomen. Let us look at a few simple ways to strengthen the kidneys, the sexual function and the gate of destiny, using qi gong to strengthen the energy in the lower sea of qi and meditations to untie the knot of Brahma.

Physical Exercise:

1 With the palms of the hands rub the area behind the waist, create friction so that the hands become warm, the lower back energised. With a loose fist pat the kidneys and lower back (Fig. 52).

2 Place the hands over the kidneys and stretch back (Fig. 53). Breathe in as you return to the upright position, then exhale deeply as you bend forwards to the floor (Fig. 54). Try to keep the knees straight, as this will stretch the kidney and bladder meridians which run down the back of the leg (Fig. 55). Repeat three times.

Qi Exercise:

1 Stand in the basic qi gong position, with the feet rooted to the ground, the lower spine straightened and the tailbone moved forwards. (See instructions for the basic qi gong position on page 140.) Simply adopting this basic position is a good way to strengthen the lower abdomen and create a sense of stability and grounding. Imagine the kidney meridian flowing through the sole of the foot and into the depths of the earth. Like the roots of a plant it draws nourishment and stability from the earth.

2 Place the hands over the lower abdomen. Breathe deeply.

Observe the rise and fall of the abdomen with the breath. Concentrate to the lower abdomen, allow the breath to descend, the diaphragm relax.

3 With an inhalation, allow the hands to move away from the abdomen, as if the filling of breath/energy were creating a large ball. Gently hold the ball with your hands in front of the abdomen. Exhale, but keep the hands holding the ball, palms facing the belly at a comfortable distance from the body. Relax the shoulders, relax the arms. Continue breathing gently in and out. Close your eyes or lower your eyelids. Just be mindful of the breath and the gentle rise and fall of the abdomen.

4 Slowly become aware of the relationship between the energy centres in the lower abdomen and the palms of the hands. Keep your awareness of the soles of the feet and their relation to the ground.

5 Retain the position for as long as you can. If your arms tire, try to release tension. (For fuller instruction see the standing exercise for the lower cinnabar field on page 155.)

Zen Breathing Exercise:

1 Lie on the floor with the knees bent and the feet flat on the floor close to the buttocks. Rest the hands over the lower abdomen (Fig. 56).

2 Breathe in deeply and feel the abdomen expand with the inhalation. Imagine that you are filling the belly with breath.

3 Breathe out and feel the abdomen contract.

Consciously move the concentration to the lower abdomen, concentrate solely on the breath. Count each

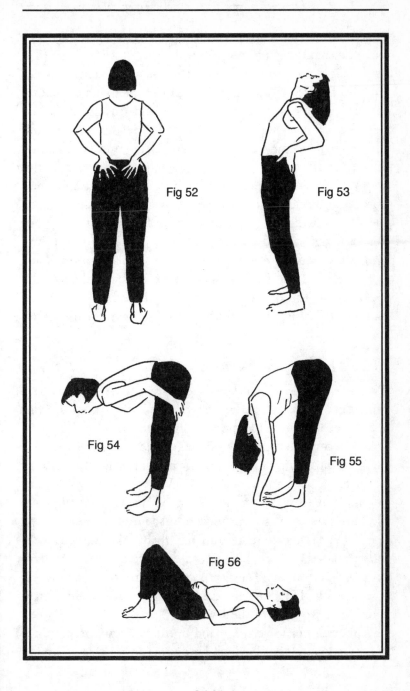

Fig 52

Fig 53

Fig 54

Fig 55

Fig 56

breath cycle until you reach ten. Begin again at one. Lengthen and deepen the breath.

This is a good preparation for all breathing exercises but can also be used as a preparation for sleep. Concentration on the lower abdomen calms the heart and the mind. Steady deep breathing brings rhythm to those deeply unconscious processes of sleeping and waking, digesting and assimilating. If you are using the exercise as a preparation for sleep, do not attempt to lengthen the breath, just breath naturally and deeply, counting the breath as you would count sheep. Keep the focus on the lower abdomen, and if thoughts enter your head, just brush them aside and continue counting. Sometimes we are not even aware that concentration is lost until we suddenly find ourselves back in the middle of the problems of the day – the conversation you wish you had had. Gently bring the mind back to the present, back to the breath.

Untying the Knot of Brahma

The knot of Brahma covers the first two chakras and represents the obstruction to progress that comes from attachment to material possessions, ambitions and desires. Based in our fears for survival and our instincts to grasp, this obstruction underlies much of present day motivation. Security is the mantra recited by TV advertisements. We are encouraged to make provision for the future, for any possible illness or event. Vast profits are made by playing on these fears. If I discuss my decisions not to have insurance or an index-related pension plan, not to use vaccinations or undergo the recommended health checks, I am considered to be irresponsible. If I deny the same things to my child, I may soon be acting against the law.

Opportunities for change and transformation are few in a society addicted to security. Our desire for life, our desire for adventure, our desire for progress can move us forward. But we cannot insure for a safe journey. Overcoming the first obstruction involves letting go of fears; letting go of our identification with the purely physical manifestation of life. Once we know that we are more than just a physical body, once we catch a glimpse of our vast and limitless possibilities, our fears no longer have a place. Once we really begin to understand what it means to trust the universe, the knot of Brahma begins to untie.

In India, the sannyasin, or spiritual seeker, traditionally gives up home and possessions. Wandering with a begging bowl is also a way of life for many Buddhist monks in the Far East. Many of us today are attempting to live in the world without being completely of the world. We are attempting to live with homes and possessions, but not to be owned by those possessions. To live with non-attachment to the physical does not mean that you have to give it all up, but it does mean to live with a lightness and freedom that does not attach importance to status, to wealth, to security. It also means developing a relationship with the body that is lighter and more fluid. If we instil fear in the body it will often react with illness. If we react to the slightest change in the body with fear, that change will be magnified and take hold. We need to develop a lightness of being which enables us to trust the natural processes of the body while also developing an increasing awareness of possible change and transformation.

But the knot of Brahma is more than a symbolic representation of attachment and desire; these mental and emotional tendencies also manifest as energetic blockages, and occasionally as physical blockages. As always when deal-ing with subtle energies, we are working with the interface between the mental/emotional and physical. If you are able to concentrate to the subtle energy channels, you may find that you become aware of an area of imbalance at a particular point. It may also manifest itself as involuntary movement of the body. Meditations to untie the knot of Brahma involve concentration of the mind and focusing the breath. It is important to use the mind to look at the attachments, to bring them into awareness. In a still and concentrated state it is possible to see the self as something other than the body. With this awareness, attachments to the material world begin to dissolve.

Method:

1 Sit in one of the meditation positions, with the spine erect and the chin slightly tucked in. Place the hands on the knees. Close the eyes, and bring the inner focus to the lower abdomen. Be aware of this as your root, your connection to the earth. Feel still and feel steady as you breathe naturally.

2 Focus the attention on the base chakra. Be aware that consciousness at this level is easily bound by bodily consciousness and the need for security. Feel your body resting on the floor; be aware that although you inhabit this body, you are more than the body. Remember that coming back to your true nature is a process of releasing all fear and insecurity; that true security is to have a deep trust in the processes of the universe and to be centred in oneself.

3 Visualise the yantra diagram of the base chakra. The lingam within the petals of the yantra represents the knot of Brahma. As you inhale slowly, imagine the breath circling around the lingam in an anti-clockwise direction. As you exhale, imagine the breath circling around the lingam in a clockwise direction (Fig. 57).

4 Visualise the prana within the breath as you inhale and

214

exhale. The prana is in the form of light. Imagine that the breath is able to untie the knot of Brahma.

OPENING THE HEART

The middle cinnabar field is in the area of the heart. The Indian term for the heart centre, 'anahata', means the inner sound, the cosmic sound or vibration that sustains all others, the rhythm of the universe. Within Chinese medicine it is the centre for the rhythm of the breath, the rhythm of the heart beat. It is the place of the fire element, which moves upwards to heaven. It houses the spirit, and is the seat of the mind and emotions. It is the upper sea of qi, from which the blood, energy and consciousness circulate through the channels of communication.

The Daoists speak of the heart as a still clear pool which is able to reflect reality. The emotions are like stones dropped into the pool – left alone the ripples will subside, clarity will be re-established.

In Zen, the heart is the empty cup waiting to be filled. Zen meditation aims to still the heart and mind while remaining rooted in the reality of the world. The Heart Sutra teaches the vanity of the world of name and form when compared to emptiness.

The knot of Vishnu located at the heart centre represents the obstruction of emotional attachment. Vishnu represents the force of preservation in the universe, the force that keeps things as they are. This force is necessary for stability, but at times it needs to be untied to allow the possibility of progress. Vishnu also symbolises family and tradition, and untying the knot of Vishnu may allow us to go beyond traditions and emotional family ties. It also suggests that we can break out of the tendencies and limitations inherited from our ancestors through the genetic code. We can transcend the limitations of the past.

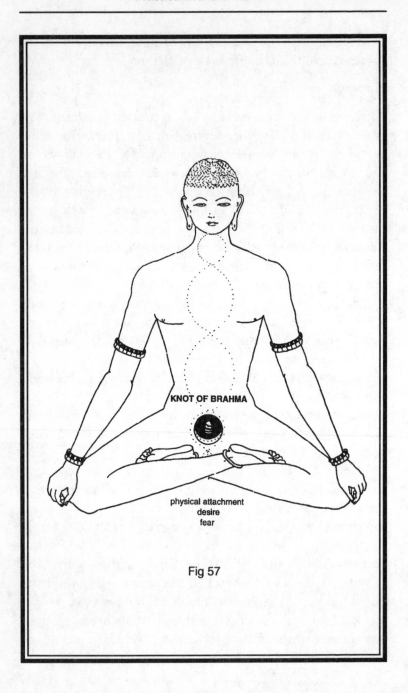

Fig 57

Working with the middle cinnabar field creates emotional stability, it allows the heart to open to the needs of others in true compassion. True compassion arises when distinctions between the self and other begin to dissolve.

Whereas the lower centres need solidity, warmth and strength, the heart centre needs fluidity, openness and expansion. The following exercises will help to bring flexibility to the upper spine, rhythm to the breath and stillness to the mind.

The Cobra:

1 Lie on the floor face downwards. Place the hands palms down on the floor to the side of the shoulders. Breathe deeply and evenly, the palms of the hands and the forehead in contact with the floor.

2 Breathe in deeply, and with an exhalation slowly bring the head up, stretching forwards and upwards to extend the neck and the upper spine. Look upwards and backwards. Once the head is off the floor begin to bring the shoulders and chest off the floor, retaining the stretch in the neck. Continue bending backwards with the upper body, supporting the weight with the hands. The navel should remain in contact with the floor (Fig. 58).

3 Remain in the extended position, breathing naturally for a few moments. Look backwards with the eyes.

4 Exhale as you slowly lower the chest to the ground, uncurl the neck and allow the forehead to rest on the floor. Repeat three times, resting between each extension.

After completing three stretches, sit back on your legs and stretch forwards. Relax with the forehead resting on the ground (Fig. 59).

Simplified Position:

If the upper spine is stiff, it may be useful to perform the above exercise in a simplified position, this is sometimes called the sphinx pose.

1 Lie on the stomach with the forehead resting on the floor. Put the forearms on the ground, the elbows close to the shoulders. Repeat the exercise as above. This position is quite comfortable and can be held for some time. Adjust the position of the arms to feel comfortable, though maintaining the stretch in the upper spine (Fig. 60).

Gentle Rotations for the Upper Spine:

1 Choosing one of the above positions, perform the exercise as above.

2 When the spine is extended, inhale and with an exhalation turn the head to look over the left shoulder towards the right foot. Keep breathing. Return to the centre (Fig. 61).

3 Inhale, and with an exhalation, turn the head to look over the right shoulder towards the left foot. Keep breathing. Return to centre.

4 Repeat the whole exercise three times.

Each time you complete three stretches, sit back on your legs and stretch forwards. Relax with the forehead resting on the ground (Fig. 59).

Breathing with Open Chest:

1 Lie on your back on the floor. Place a roll (a cushion or rolled towel will do) under the shoulder blades. The tops of the shoulders should rest on the floor. If the neck is not

Fig 58

Fig 59

Fig 60

Fig 61

Fig 62

comfortable, rest the head on a small cushion or pad. Rotate the arms backwards slightly in their sockets and place the back of the arms and the backs of the hands on the floor at shoulder level. This helps to open the chest (Fig. 62).

2   Feel the weight of the body heavy on the floor and allow the whole body to relax. Close your eyes. Relax the eyes, relax the tongue, relax the brain.

3   Breathe deeply and evenly, with awareness of the breath as it passes through the nose. Make the breath very light and gentle. Try not to make any noise, just a quiet awareness of the sensation of the breath in the nostrils, in the throat, in the lungs.

4   Feel the rib cage gently expanding with the inhalation, relaxing with the exhalation. Make no effort to control the breath, just breathe naturally, constantly observing the sensation in the nostrils, the throat, the movement of the chest.

5   As you bring the exercise to a close, take two or three deep breaths. Roll on to your side and remain there for a few minutes before you get up.

Qi Exercise:

While remaining rooted in the basic qi gong position, the gentle movements of 'cloud hands' keep the mind focused and the upper spine flexible.

1   Stand in the basic qi gong position (see page 140), feet rooted to the ground, knees slightly bent and the tailbone tucked forwards. Once the lower body feels strong and stable,

stretch the spine upwards with the chin tucked in and the back of the neck extended.

2 Loosen up the upper body by swinging the arms from side to side; keep the lower body still as the spine rotates.

3 Shake the shoulders and arms, then bring the hands to face the front of the body – the left palm facing the upper chest, the right palm facing downwards at the level of the navel (Fig. 63).

4 Move the upper body to the left, as you rotate the hands until the palms are facing each other (Fig. 64).

5 As you move back towards the centre, move the right hand up, the left hand down, until you are facing forwards with the right hand facing your upper chest, the left hand facing downwards at the level of the navel (Fig. 65).

6 Repeat the movement towards the left (Fig. 66) until you are back to the centre with the hands as in position 3.

Repeat positions 4, 5 and 6 until you have established a rhythm. As with much of qi gong, it is difficult to explain, but very easy to do.

Once you have established a good rhythm, this exercise can be performed for some time. It is one of the most effective moving meditations. The hands describe the tai ji symbol, with its continual movement between yin and yang. Be aware of the centre of the palm, where the heart meridian emits energy. Be aware of the flow of energy from the centre of the chest to the palms of the hands.

When you finish the exercise, gently bring the hands to rest over the heart.

Untying the Knot of Vishnu

Whereas the knot of Brahma and the energy of the lower centres is said to nurture the physical body, the knot of Vishnu nurtures the subtle bodies. The mental body is said to be nourished by mental and emotional energy. Once the knot of Vishnu is untied the division between the self and the cosmos is broken, the energy of the individual resonates with the energy of the cosmos.

The energy centre of the heart inspires love, compassion, faith, devotion and duty. This can be the positive aspect of the knot of Vishnu, but once these attributes no longer aid progress, but keep one bound, the knot of Vishnu may need to be untied. As the force of preservation, Vishnu keeps things as they are. The knot of Vishnu creates the desire to preserve spiritual traditions and institutions, but even faith in a teaching, devotion to a guru, the desire to help others can become an attachment.

We tend to equate compassion with good works, with the desire to help others. But true compassion is feeling with others. It is the natural state when the boundaries between the self and other are dissolved. One can have a true compassion for nature when there is no boundary between oneself and the cosmos.

The difficulty in untying the knot of Vishnu lies in its relationship to the genetic code. In Chinese medicine the energy located in this area at the centre of the chest is called the ancestral energy. This is the energy that keeps intact the lineage, the ancestral heritage, the genetic code. We not only inherit physical attributes from our parents and grandparents, but may also carry many of the emotional characteristics of our ancestors. In the East this may be referred to as family karma. In India when a sannyasin, or spiritual aspirant, comes to this point in his initiation, the family will

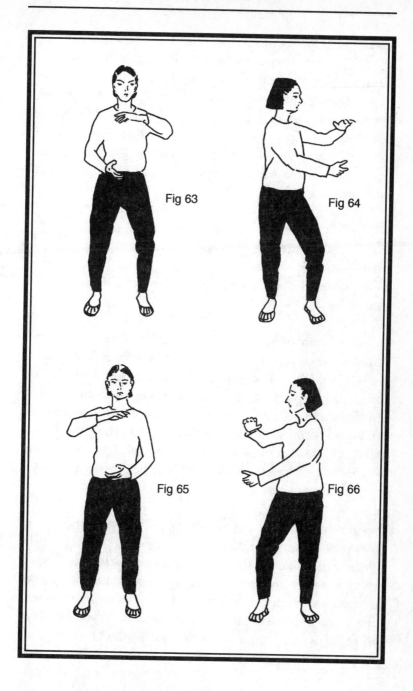

Fig 63

Fig 64

Fig 65

Fig 66

traditionally perform funeral rites. This is to allow the sannyasin freedom from deep family ties which go beyond the conscious mind and may keep the seeker bound to the past.

It is the merging of individual self with the divine which is achieved by untying the knot of Vishnu. The old self, based in old beliefs, old traditions and family values, gives way to a new self – limitless and free. This is the discovery of the true nature, free of old habits and the restraints of the past, living in accordance with the way of heaven, the Dao.

Meditation:

1   Sitting in a meditation position, make sure that the spine is straight. Rest the hands on the knees and close the eyes. Breathe deeply and evenly until the body feels still and calm.

2   Focus your awareness at the heart centre, the anahata chakra, the upper sea of qi. Consciousness at this level is easily bound by emotional ties to family, friends, traditions, teachers. Be aware of the bondage brought about by those emotional ties. We all feel emotion, but try to imagine that emotion can flow through you without affecting your inner calm. Realise that although you may experience emotions, you are not those emotions. Your true being is not touched by those emotions.

3   Be aware that you are part of the cosmos. Feel the cosmic sound and vibration in the rhythm of the breath, the beating of the heart. Know that all beings are part of that same cosmic rhythm. You are not a separate individual but part of the universal creation. As the self begins to merge with the divine consciousness, resistance is released. As we let go of old patterns and habits, old belief systems and teachings we can open to the light of the truth.

4 Visualise the yantra diagram of the anahata chakra. The red lingam within the six-pointed star of the yantra represents the knot of Vishnu. As you inhale slowly, imagine the breath circling around the lingam in a clockwise direction. As you exhale, imagine the breath circling around the lingam in an anti-clockwise direction (Fig. 67).

5 Visualise the prana within the breath as you inhale and exhale. The prana is in the form of light. Imagine that the breath is able to untie the knot of Vishnu.

6 After five rounds of inhalation and exhalation, breathe naturally.

FREEING THE MIND

The upper cinnabar field, the energy centre between the eyebrows, is the place of the true self, the inner guide – our access to the intuitive mind and to universal wisdom. The third eye is known in many cultures as the eye of knowledge and vision, which is able to see past, present and future.

In the Chinese alchemical body map it is the place where Lao zi sits in meditation; the place beyond the division of yin and yang, beyond duality – the place of the impartial observer, the true alchemist. It is above the influence of the five elements which create movement and transformation within the physical and energy bodies.

In the Indian tradition it is the ajna chakra, ajna meaning to know and to command. Its trigger point is between the eyebrows but its root is deep within the brain at the pineal gland. In the Indian system this is also seen as the place above duality and the place above the interactions of the five elements. Here the ida and pingala nadis, the lunar and solar channels, merge and dissolve into each other. It is the centre

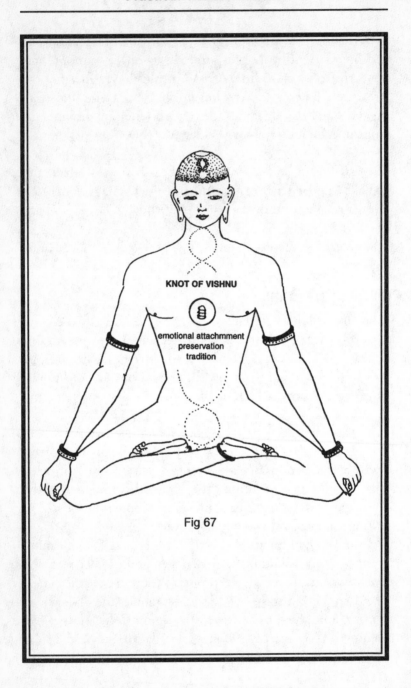

KNOT OF VISHNU

emotional attachmment
preservation
tradition

Fig 67

of consciousness which relates to the causal body, which is above the distinction of gender. It exists outside time and space. It is also above karma.

Situated at the centre between the eyebrows is the knot of Rudra, sometimes called the knot of Shiva. This is the last knot which creates a blockage between the brow centre and the crown centre. The crown centre represents complete union with divine consciousness.

Working with the upper dan tian brings mental clarity. It allows us to rise above the demands of the body and the emotions and to see with detachment. Once we access this part of our mind, it can act as our guide, our contact with intuitive wisdom.

When working with the brow centre, physical exercise does not seem to be appropriate, although it is important to ensure that the energy channels flowing through the neck and shoulders are free of obstruction. The following sequence of exercises ensures freeflow of energy into the head, the brain and the sensory orifices. Sit comfortably with the spine straight, or stand in the basic qi gong position.

1 Shoulders: with the hands hanging loosely at the side, pull the shoulders up towards the ears, then let them go, releasing any tension. Keep the shoulders straight, not hunching forward, or stretching back. Repeat five times. Bring the hands to the shoulders and rotate the arms, bringing the elbows together, then stretching away in as large a circle as possible. Repeat the opposite way (Fig. 68).

2 Shoulder massage: with the right elbow loosely supported in the palm of the left hand, make a fist with the right hand and gently tap the top and back of the left shoulder. Release the fist and tap the shoulders with the palm. Make

sure that the elbow is well supported and the hand completely relaxed. Repeat for the opposite side (Fig. 69).

3 Neck stretches: with the hands relaxed in the lap, breathe quietly. Take a breath in and exhaling bring the chin down to the chest. This should be a slow controlled movement, co-ordinated with the breath. Breathe in and return to the upright position. Breathe out as you allow the head to fall backwards. These movements should always be slow and controlled, allowing the weight of the head to stretch the muscles. Repeat for ten full breaths, five complete movements (Fig. 70).

4 Relax and take a few breaths. Breathe in and as you exhale, allow the head to fall slowly to the side, bringing the ear towards the shoulder. Do not force. Breathe in as you bring the head back to the central position. Repeat on the other side. A very gentle movement is sufficient to stimulate the meridians and to relax the muscles. Repeat for ten full breaths, five complete movements (Fig. 71).

5 Relax again at the centre. Take a deep breath in. Keeping the head vertical, slowly rotate the head around to look over your right shoulder as you exhale. Keep the eyes open wide and look around as far as you can to the back. Make sure that the top of your head remains in the centre, the neck stretches upwards as if being pulled by a rope from the top of the head, the chin is pulled slightly in. As you breathe in, slowly bring the head back to the centre. Breathe out and move slowly to the left. Repeat for ten breaths, five complete movements (Fig. 72).

6 Ears: rub the hands together until they are warm and place them over the ears. With the thumb and index finger pull the ear lobes, then gently squeeze around the rim of the

Fig 68

Fig 69

Fig 71

Fig 70

Fig 72

Fig 74

Fig 75

Fig 73

Fig 76

ear. With the hands still loosely over the ears, allow the thumbs to rest in the hollow behind the ears at the base of the skull. Keeping the shoulders relaxed, gently push the thumbs upwards. Relax and repeat, breathing out as you stretch the neck (Fig. 73).

7   Eyes: sitting in a relaxed position with the spine straight, rub the hands together vigorously until they are hot. Place the hands over the eyes, the centre of the palm over the centre of the eyeball. Remain still for two to three minutes with the eyes closed. Repeat three times (Fig. 74). With the thumb and forefinger, pinch along the eyebrows, from the centre outwards (Fig. 75).

8   Head: shake the hands with the wrist loose. Keeping that same loose action, lift the hands above the head, and pat the head with the fingertips, beginning at the centre front and working slowly to the nape of the neck; gradually separate the hands and repeat, moving about an inch further from the centre line each time (Fig. 76).

9   With the same loose wrist movement, tap the base of the skull with the fingertips.

10   Qi Sweeping: place the palms of the hands over the eyes, then stroke the hands backwards, around the head, down the back of the neck, across the shoulders and down the front of the body in one long sweeping movement, as if you are brushing the body down. Repeat three times and remain sitting quietly for a few moments.

Qi Gong:

The qi gong exercise for balancing the three cinnabar fields is a good exercise to ensure an even flow of energy through the primary yin and yang channels, and as preparation for concentration to the brow centre.

Assume the basic qi gong stance. Bring the awareness to the soles of the feet and the palms of the hands. Place the hands over the abdomen, just below the navel and relax. As you extend the lower spine and tuck the tailbone into the body you will feel a slight contraction in the lower abdomen. Try to become aware of the feeling and keep it throughout the practice.

1 Slowly separate the hands, hold them about six inches from the body, palms facing the abdomen. With an inhalation slowly move the hands up to the level of the chest and over the top of the head, the elbows will bend naturally.

2 As you breathe out the hands move over the back of the head, over the shoulders, then push down to the lower abdomen.

3 Turn the hands upwards and begin the movement again, keeping in rhythm with the breath.

As you perform the simple movements, focus your mind on the primary yin and yang channels. With the in-breath, imagine the energy flowing up the front of the body, over the abdomen, through the heart, the throat and into the brow centre. With the out-breath, imagine the breath circulating over the back of the head and down the spine.

Continue for at least ten complete cycles, then gradually bring the movement back to the centre, bringing the hands to rest on the lower abdomen. Remain still for a few moments, reconnecting with the centre in the lower abdomen and with the soles of the feet. When your breath is even and your body quite still, move the limbs and the shoulders and then relax.

Sitting Meditation:

Sit in a comfortable meditation position. If you are sitting on a chair, make sure the soles of the feet are flat on the floor. Keep your hands in your lap, your spine straight.

1 Breathe gently while focusing your attention to the lower abdomen. Allow the abdomen to rise and fall with the inhalation and exhalation of the breath.

2 Bring the attention to the base of the spine. With an inhalation imagine the breath moving through the spinal channel to the base of the skull, over the top of the head and to the brow centre.

3 Be aware of the brow centre as you hold your breath for a few seconds.

4 Exhale and imagine that the breath is moving down the front channel, back to the perineum.

Complete ten rounds, gently inhaling and exhaling.

5 Bring the awareness to the base chakra. Imagine the breath moving in and out of this centre. Feel strength and solidity.

6 Bring the awareness to the heart centre. Imagine that the breath is moving in and out of the heart centre. Feel calm and peace. Imagine the heart as a still pool of deep water. A water lily floats on the pool, its petals open in perfect symmetry.

7 Bring the awareness to the brow centre. Feel open and light. Feel yourself expand beyond the body as you leave the

constraints of the world of duality. Breathe in and out through the brow centre. As you breathe in, fill the head with light, as you breathe out extend the breath into the universe. Gently hold the concentration on the brow centre. Do not strain, constantly relax the eyes, relax the forehead.

If tension develops in the head at any time, bring the concentration back to the lower abdomen.

Untying the Knot of Shiva

To the Indian mystic, the knot of Shiva controls the ability to see past, present and future. It brings gifts of vision and clairvoyance. But these very gifts can become an obstacle to progress and yoga theory constantly reminds us that it is not these powers that we are seeking. What we are trying to attain is an unobstructed pathway between the physical and the divine. What we are aiming for is a channel that is open to pure consciousness and a physical body that is progressively more adaptable and receptive to it.

The ajna chakra is the centre of thoughts and visions. It concerns the transformation of thoughts and ideas from the personal into the universal. It opens the mind to intuition. Sri Aurobindo suggests that to make the next evolutionary leap, mankind will give up its present over-concentration on the intellect, as we learn to rely more on intuition. By concentration on the knot of Shiva, we can begin to be detached from the mind. We can begin to see the limitations of the mind. As we loosen the mind's hold over us we can begin to experience other realities. Our mind is often our greatest limitation.

Method:

1   Sit in one of the meditation positions, with the spine erect and the chin slightly tucked in. Place the hands on the knees.

Close the eyes, and bring the inner focus to the lower abdomen. Be aware of this as your root, your connection to the earth. Feel still and feel steady as you breathe naturally.

2 Focus the attention in the brow centre. Be aware of the body; know that although you inhabit this body, you are more than the body. Experience your feelings; know that although you may experience feelings, you are more than your feelings. Observe your thoughts. Know that you are more than your thoughts, more than your mind. Release your thoughts. Be aware of your higher nature. Be aware that you are pure consciousness.

3 Raise the awareness through the sushumna passage to the ajna chakra. Concentrate on the yantra of the ajna chakra, which is a black lingam inside a two-petalled flower.

4 As you inhale, imagine that the breath is rotating around the lingam three times in an anti-clockwise direction. As you exhale, imagine the breath circling around the lingam in a clockwise direction (Fig. 77).

5 Visualise the prana within the breath as you inhale and exhale. The prana is in the form of light. Imagine that the breath is able to untie the knot of Shiva.

6 Practise this five times. After the last breath, sit quietly. Imagine that a white light is descending through the crown chakra, filling the head, filling the body. Sit bathed in white light. Become one with the light of pure consciousness.

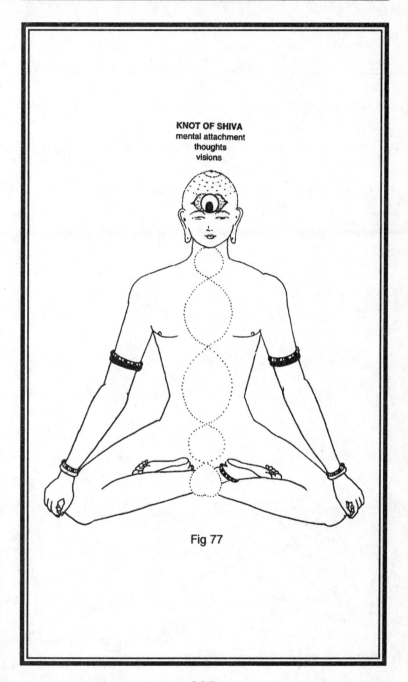

Fig 77

Conclusion

Life is a process of continual transformation. It is the way of nature. But that does not mean that change is always easy. Physically, mentally and emotionally, we often prefer the comfort of the familiar. Sometimes we put up with intense pain and suffering rather than change our habits. More often we are slowly stifled in situations which deny our growth. In our modern world where many of the old causes of disease have been eradicated, we find that physical illness is often rooted in a sickness of the soul and a failure to follow our true nature.

The practices presented in this book aim to align us with our original pattern, to allow our energy to flow freely, to take us closer to who we really are. They maintain that by finding our own centre, by strengthening our roots and opening our hearts, we are able to fully engage in life. The exercises are often very simple, but it is the commitment to practice, the commitment to consciousness which creates change.

In the past care for the soul was often carried out in a monastic environment where the individual could concentrate on the work at hand without concern for the world outside. Each system has its own rules and regulations which were for the protection of the practitioner and in some cases the protection of the system. Nowadays there is a tendency to question authority and to move away from the dominance of the spiritual hierarchy and the male guru. There is an obvious shift back to the feminine – which means that more respect is given to the earth and more respect is given to the body. We are no longer searching for an escape from this world and looking towards paradise in the next, but slowly beginning to see that transformation needs to happen here.

We are no longer trying to separate matter and consciousness by annulling the creation, but attempting to allow consciousness to manifest itself in the material world.

It is as if we are on the edge of spiritual maturity, but not quite able to let go of the guiding hand of the past. So while looking to the traditions of the past, let us attempt to find methods of practice which are suitable for our lives in the twenty-first century. Let us try to use the wisdom of the ancient traditions without developing rigidity. Let us go back to the roots of the teachings in order to know what we are doing and why. Then maybe we can change and adapt the practice for our own needs. We need to question. We need to develop integrity. We need to learn to listen to our intuition as to whether a path feels right or wrong. This is the beginning of spiritual maturity.

If we act wisely – keeping our own integrity, while not damaging the integrity of others – we may begin to move on to the next stage of our soul's journey. If we learn to trust our own inner guidance, we come closer to our own path – rather than being sidetracked to somebody else's. In order to be effective practitioners today, our most precious and indispensable tool is self-responsibility. If we are able to be responsible for ourselves, we can truly relate to others.

Glossary of Chinese and Sanskrit Terms

asana	yoga posture
Ayurveda	the Indian science of medicine according to the Vedas or ancient scriptures
chakra	centre of energy transformation (Indian)
cinnabar field	centre of energy transformation (Chinese)
dan tian	cinnabar field
Dao	the way, that which is natural, the true nature
dosha	body and constitutional type according to Ayurveda
essences	most subtle form of matter
feng shui	literally 'wind water', the Chinese science of geomancy
gate of destiny	the origin of our inherited energies, the place from which life emerges and returns
hara	the belly, the energy centre in the lower abdomen (Japanese)
heaters, three	the three areas of energy production in Chinese medicine, the lower abdomen, the upper abdomen and the chest
ida (nadi)	energy channel located within the spine
jing	essences, the most subtle form of matter
jingshen	essence and spirit, vitality
koan	zen exercise for the mind

kundalini	shakti, the feminine side of Brahman; the evolutionary force within matter
meridian	energetic pathway, information channel
moxibustion	the therapeutic use of heat on specific acupuncture points
nadi	energetic pathway, information channel (sanskrit)
ojas	essences, sexual essences (sanskrit)
pingala (nadi)	subtle energy channel within the spine
po	physical consciousness
prana	subtle energy (sanskrit)
qi	subtle energy (Chinese)
qi gong	working with qi
rishi	Indian saint or yogi
shen	spirit or spirits (Chinese)
shiatsu	therapeutic massage on the energy channels and acupuncture points (Japanese)
spirits	the beneficial influence of heaven
sushumna	central energy channel within the spine (sanskrit)
tai ji	great ridge pole, as in the tai ji quan (tai chi chuan) and the pole star
tejas	subtle fire, digestive fire (sanskrit)
trigram	symbol of broken and unbroken lines relating to yin and yang; the combination of two trigrams forming the hexagrams of the Book of Change
yang	relating to heaven, energy and movement (Chinese)
yantra	pattern or symbol of subtle energy (sanskrit)
yin	relating to earth, matter and stability (Chinese)

Index

241